16/=

Tales from
Mount Kenya

Tales from Mount Kenya

NGUMBU NJURURI

Illustrations and cover design by
Adrienne Kennaway

TRANSAFRICA PUBLISHERS

The first edition of these stories was published by
OXFORD UNIVERSITY PRESS, LONDON
in 1966 under the title *Agikuyu Folk Tales*

This second edition is published by
TRANSAFRICA PUBLISHERS LIMITED
KENWOOD HOUSE, KIMATHI STREET,
P.O. BOX 42990, NAIROBI, KENYA

Printed in Kenya by
PRINTING AND PACKAGING CORPORATION LIMITED
P.O. BOX 30157, LIKONI ROAD, NAIROBI

Dedication

To my late beloved mother,
Wahito Mwari wa Kuira, to Gikuyu and Mumbi,
the father and mother of the Agikuyu, and to all Kenyans
living and dead who cherish and uphold our national
heritage; may they all unite in the spirit of Harambee
in the reconstruction and perpetuation of
the destroyed shrines.

Contents

The Ogress and the Blacksmith's Wife *?family & VIP.*   I

The Girl and the Ogre *foolish girls*   5

Konyeki and his Father the Ogre *a way to escape?*   12

Mwithanga and the Great River Monster   15

The Land of the Spirits *[An angel light .. things aren't as they appear — spirits do not offer life]*   17

The Woman and the Bird *[Do unto others ...]*   21

The Baboons and the Village Women *Can a Leopard change its spots?*   25

The Story of Hyena and Squirrel   30

Hare and the Well in the Jungle   33

How the Wild Turkey got its Spots   36

The Great Famine and the Law of the Jungle   38

The Story of Mwathi and his Creditors   42

The Twilight Song of Honey-bird   56

The Man and the Dove   59

The Girl and the Drought   63

The Girl and her Father's Gourd   66

The Monster that Never Was   68

The Poor Man of Iruri   71

The Story of Moon and Sun   74

The Boy and Nyange the Cow   84

Wacici and her Friends *(kikuyu female Joseph)*   90

The Wise Man and his Sons *united we stand*   94

Wacu and the Eagle   99

The Story of Ragai and his Wife   103

Wahome and the First White Hunter   III

Acknowledgements

The author is grateful to Mrs Mary Knapp for her encourage-
ment and help, and to Mr Waithaka Gakere for telling him
some of these folk tales.

The Ogress and the Blacksmith's Wife

ONCE upon a time there was a blacksmith who lived on a lonely hill with his wife. His forge was in a distant village and sometimes he used to stay there for several months working while his wife stayed at home.

His wife was expecting a child. He bought a ram, food, and everything that was necessary for her as the African custom required, and these things were intended to help her to rebuild her strength after the birth. He went away to work and stayed there for some months. Carelessly, however, Muturi the blacksmith neglected to calculate the date the child would arrive, and his wife gave birth to a baby boy while he was away.

Whilst she was in the throes of giving birth, she screamed and shouted for help, but as her home was a long way from any others in the village, no one heard her.

Now there was a notorious ogress who roamed over the hills and in the forests around them. She happened to hear Muturi's wife calling out. At once she realized that the woman must be alone and giving birth to a child. She decided to disguise herself by magic as a human being and go to help the mother in labour.

When she got there she helped to bath the baby and cooked some food for the mother. Muturi's wife was very grateful to her and decided to ask the saintly woman to stay on for some days until her husband returned. The ogress learnt all about the husband and when he was expected to return home and she decided first to feast on the nice food left for his wife and finally to kill her and the baby and eat them up.

When the food was nearly finished the ogress decided not to give the mother nor the baby any food at all. She herself ate everything that she cooked and whenever Muturi's wife complained, she threatened to kill her. Then Muturi's wife realized that the stranger was an ogress, and that her life and her baby's were in grave danger.

One morning while the terrible ogress was away in the forest gathering firewood, Muturi's wife saw a dove outside the house. She gave it some grain and begged it to fly to the village of the blacksmiths and tell her husband that she had given birth to a baby boy, that her nurse was an ogress and that her life and that of the baby were in danger.

Surprisingly enough the dove answered pleasantly and promised the woman that because of her kindness and generosity it was going to take the message to her husband at once, and that she must not worry as she would be saved.

The dove flew away proudly and for a moment the woman thought she was dreaming as she saw it disappear over the horizon.

That night she lay awake expecting and hoping her husband would arrive at any moment. God had heard her prayers and sent the dove to take her message to her husband. She was immensely relieved and began to regain her confidence.

The dove arrived at the blacksmiths' village and perched on top of Muturi's smithy. There it sang in a most beautiful voice quite unlike anything ever heard before. When the blacksmiths heard it they all stopped working and in the still silence they could hear:

> *Muturi ugutura i! Cangairu cangairukia;*
> *Tura tura narua i! Cangairu cangairukia;*
> *Mukaguo anaciara i! Cangairu cangairukia,*
> *Aciaritho ni irimu i! Cangairu cangairukia.*

> You blacksmith working,
> Who left your wife expecting,
> Hurry up, hurry up,
> Go home quickly, quickly,

Your wife has got a baby,
Being nursed by an ogress,
So hurry up, hurry up,
Go back quickly, quickly.

At first they could not understand what it all meant. They listened again and at last someone understood and at once asked,

'Who left his wife expecting a baby?'

This time Muturi remembered that his wife was expecting a baby and it was due about that time. He took his spear, sword, bow, and arrows and, wasting no time, he made off for home. He walked through thick forests by night and arrived home the following morning just after the ogress had gone to the forest to fetch firewood as usual. When his wife told him of her terrible ordeal, he decided to hide somewhere above the ceiling near the door and said he would slash the ogress with his razor-sharp sword as she entered the house.

When the ogress came back with firewood she dropped it outside and shouted a curse on the miserable mother in the house.

'May the woman in this house drop down like these bits of wood!' The wife simply answered,

'May you also drop down like that!' When the ogress heard this she said scornfully,

'You speak as though all the blacksmiths have arrived; have they?'

'They have not come yet,' said Muturi's wife, 'but I can't stand your treatment of me any longer!' The ogress, annoyed with the woman's behaviour, rushed into the house intending to kill her. Suddenly Muturi jumped on her with his sharp sword and hacked off her head with one stroke. He slashed her into pieces and burnt her into ashes with the firewood she had brought from the forest.

His wife was greatly relieved and after that he looked after her and his son tenderly and never stayed away from home so long again.

3

The Girl and the Ogre

Young boys and girls in Africa used to perform their traditional dances in the summer, after the harvesting season. They would go to distant places to dance. An arrangement would then be made for one group to organize a similar occasion and boys and girls from other places would then visit them in return.

It happened one day that six girls left their home without being escorted by their partners and went a long way away to dance. At this place it was said that dangerous ogres, magically disguised in size and shape like men, would join in the dancing and in the end succeed in persuading some of the girls to go with them to their homes. Many girls lost their lives, and for a long time nobody knew where they had gone or what had happened to them.

On one particular occasion, one ogre who looked the most handsome of all the men present at the dance attracted the attention of most of the girls present. Nobody suspected that he was anything but a young man from a noble family. The six girls who came without their boys were particularly interested in him. They went to him and they all danced with him in turn. The ogre was very courteous and asked them all to go to his home with him and be introduced to his mother. They did not accept at once because they thought it was getting late and they ought to return. He insisted and told them that his home was not very far and he would take them home if it got late. At this point they all seemed to agree although one of them was beginning to suspect the integrity of the young man, because

5

she had noticed something peculiar at the base of his skull, which she thought was a second mouth which is characteristic of ogres. She whispered about this to her closest friends but they all thought that she was being funny. She was right but the ogre had covered his back mouth with his elegant hair-dressing.

So off they started. But after a short distance towards the ogre's home another girl noticed this peculiar mouth, she immediately spoke to the other one who saw it first and both of them arranged to slip away and find their own way home. The four who were left continued their journey to the ogre's home, and as the ogre had not had food for many days and was so exhausted after a long day's dancing, he was beginning to betray himself. Sometimes he would stop, keep the girls busy talking in front of him, and try to gain some strength by catching any little creatures wandering near by such as mice, or cockroaches, or caterpillars, as well as absorbing into his back mouth any flies that came to cluster round it, while keeping up conversation with his front one.

All this time they were slowly walking towards a thick forest a long way away from the beautiful green dancing-field which was near their village. Another two girls became definitely suspicious and decided to slip away, like the first two. The ogre was left with only two. Shortly after the ogre and the two girls started to walk through the forest following a narrow path, one of the girls asked him why his home was in a forest. He replied that it was at the other side of the forest and that they were taking a short cut and it would take a long time to go round the forest. At this point this girl decided to escape, like her other friends. She tried to persuade the remaining one but in vain, so she finally went home alone.

The ogre was left with one girl now. She was the one who was the most attracted to him and she was even happier to be alone with him, so they went on. But as it was beginning to get dark and still no sign of a home was to be seen anywhere near, the girl, who was getting tired, began to worry. The ogre comforted her by assuring her that they were very near home, and indeed they really were. The ogre had a fine hut built in the middle of the forest.

When they arrived he asked the girl to wait outside while he went in to light the fire. She became suspicious at once, because in the first place she was made to understand that the young man's home was at the other side of the forest whereas now it turned out to be in the middle of it, and instead of finding his mother in the hut, it was empty, without a fire.

She wondered whether to run away or to wait and find out the real truth. So she waited, and listened carefully, and heard a most peculiar noise in the hut which sounded like the rattling of bones. She was right! The ogre was clearing the hut and hiding the bones away so that the girl should not suspect anything. He lit the fire, and, having made sure that everything was in order and that the place was tidy, invited the girl to come in. He gave her a nice stool to sit on and asked her to wait while he went to bring his mother from a nearby hut.

Leaving the hut the ogre fastened the door very cleverly and locked it from outside without the girl noticing that she was being imprisoned. He went away to fetch his friends to come to feast on the girl. When he got to his friends he found them with another feast, of animal flesh caught in the forest. He was invited to join in and take a little bit. He told them about his catch and asked them not to eat too much lest they should spoil their appetite, as, of course, ogres naturally prefer human flesh to that of animals.

His friends were delighted to hear the news, but they were doubtful whether it was real or false, as they had been decieved by him before. He assured them that he had caught a nice, fat girl, who was properly secured in his hut. He asked them to collect some firewood and carry their knives and go with him to his hut where they would have a better feast. They all agreed, but on condition that if they were deceived, this time they would feast on him. He took it as a joke, and even if he had taken it seriously, he was sure that he would not be eaten, since he had locked up the girl properly.

During all this time the girl had been busy spying round the hut, and to her horror and dismay she found piles of human bones hidden in it. At last she realized that her friends were right and that she was foolish. She tried to open the door to escape but it was hopeless. She cried and prayed and tried to force the walls, the roof, almost anything she could think of, but it was useless. At this point to her amazement one of the human skulls jumped from the ceiling! Landing near the fire it spoke kindly to the girl and said,

'Don't worry, my friend, I shall save your life, and tonight I shall punish the ogre who has caused so much misery to my people. I will open this door for you, and you shall go back home following the same track along which you came. On the way you will meet the ogre and his friends, who will be carrying some firewood to come here and cook you. As soon as you hear them near you, you must hide in a bush near a very broad tree, and there you will be quiet and unafraid, whatever the circumstances, until all the ogres have passed you. You will then come out on the path and track your way out of the forest.

'When you reach home, inform your parents of the presence of the dangerous ogres in this forest, and ask them to summon all the people in all the villages and warn them of this danger. They will need to organize all the warriors in every village and come to attack and destroy the ogres.'

The girl was very pleased to hear this; although it was like a nightmare to her she believed it because no sooner had the skull stopped talking than the door opened gently and she walked out as she was instructed. And as soon as she had stepped outside, the door closed and locked itself securely as before.

The girl started hurrying along the path through the forest as she had been told towards the direction she had come from. When she was about midway she heard some noise, and listening intently she realized it was the ogres as prophesied by the skull. She looked about and saw a thick bush by a very big tree, and quickly went and hid in it.

8

The ogres came along the path, led by her captor and followed by his guests in order of their seniority and rank. They were all talking about their previous good feasts of human beings and the girl could hear some of the places mentioned, so as she knew that some girls had disappeared from these places and had never been found, she realized that this was how they had met their fate.

At this point many of the ogres including the host could smell the trail of the girl. Many of them wondered whether there was another girl somewhere around and almost started searching. But the host insisted that they should hurry home before it was too late. He told them that he recognized that trail, and that it belonged to the girl whom he had taken into captivity in his hut. They believed this was her original trail, and joyfully increased their pace to go to feast on her.

But there was one multi-legged and multi-headed ogre who got confused on reaching the point of this trail, because one head would smell the trail this way and the other that way; he almost danced about on this spot, moving sideways and forward and backward, not knowing actually in which direction to go. He had almost found the girl when his host came furiously and pushed him and asked him to follow the others. Another one-legged, one-eyed little ogre also got into confusion when he came to this point, and hopping towards the direction of the girl he was stopped angrily by the host and persuaded to follow the others.

All this time the girl was quiet, although she was petrified when the terrible, horrid, multi-legged, multi-headed monster almost got on to her, and nearly screamed. But she was free and safe again. She came back out on to the track and quickly got free of the forest.

When it lay behind her she took the shortest possible way home. It was about midnight, but in the bright moonlight she could see her way about and was no longer afraid. She got home safely and fulfilled her promise to the skull by giving the message to her parents. She apologized for her behaviour. Her father joyfully forgave her and said that perhaps it had been the will of God, so that others could be saved. He immediately summoned the council of elders from all the villages to meet the following morning and plan for a siege against the ogres in the forest.

The ogres had got to the hut in the middle of the forest by this time. They piled up their firewood and asked their host to bring the girl out for slaughter. He asked them to make the fire while he went into the hut to fetch her. He unlocked the door and went inside, but of course could not find a trace of the girl. He searched all over the place and found nothing. He locked himself inside and began to worry that his friends would carry out their threat of eating him if he did not have any girl to eat in the hut. He continued his search but it was all in vain. To his surprise the talking skull jumped on to the floor and told him:

'Tonight I am going to punish you for all your crimes against my people. Your friends are going to kill you and feast on you, and they in turn shall be exterminated by the warriors of my people before the end of this moon.'

The ogre collapsed in fear. His friends outside grew impatient and kept on calling on him to bring out the prey, but getting no response they threatened to break in and get it themselves—if there was none, they would kill him and feast on him as had already been agreed. They eventually had to break in the door as there was no answer coming from the hut. They found their host lying unconscious on the floor, and finding no girl after a long and laborious search in the hut they all resolved to carry out their agreement. They dragged their host out, chopped him into pieces, and made a delicious feast out of him.

They all returned happily to their respective dwellings, fully satisfied that they had had a wonderful day. But they did not know of their own fate for the following afternoon! The whole forest was surrounded by great warriors who set it on fire, and the ogres were all killed either by spears when trying to escape or by being burnt to death in the forest.

That was the end of the dangerous monsters who for so long

caused so many miseries to mankind and it marked the beginning of real happiness for young boys and girls who loved to do their traditional dances which brought entertainment and joy to the people.

Konyeki and his Father the Ogre

ONCE upon a time an ogre married a Gikuyu girl who did not know that he was an ogre. After their wedding the bride learnt that she was married to an ogre, but now she could not leave him since he threatened to kill and eat her if she ran away, or if she told anyone that he was an ogre. She lived a most dreadful life.

One day she gave birth to a baby boy and she named him Konyeki. When Konyeki grew up he adopted his father's habits and he also became a terrible ogre. He would go to the forest to hunt with his father and they would catch all sorts of creatures and bring their catch home for her to cook. She herself never ate meat caught by them. She was a vegetarian.

Once Konyeki's aunt, that is his mother's sister, came to pay them a visit. Konyeki and his father decided to kill her at night and eat her. Konyeki's mother realized that this would happen and advised her sister to escape and return home immediately. She did not tell her sister exactly why she did not want her to stay, but just advised her very strongly to go away quickly.

Konyeki's aunt—that is how she is always referred to in the story—was very suspicious and decided to hide somewhere in the forest and spy on what was going on, out of curiosity. She climbed a broad tree and stayed on top. But when Konyeki and his father were passing by that tree Konyeki smelled the woman, and when he looked up he saw her. He tried to attract his father's attention, but without success. His father said that he did not wish to waste time and that they should hurry home. Konyeki climbed the tree. Seeing that it was his aunt whom they were going to kill and eat, he told her, 'We were going to kill and eat you tonight. If you give me your fingers and let me eat them, I shall let you go and I shall not tell my father.' She gave him her fingers. Then he demanded her toes. She became helpless as she could not cling to the tree any more. In great pain she fell down from the tree. Konyeki called his father and said, 'I have caught her, father, come and see.' When his father came, they killed her and when they opened her stomach they found three babies. They were all boys. Konyeki wrapped them carefully and took them to his mother to cook for him. They were still alive when they were taken to her. She realized what had happened, as she knew that her sister was pregnant, and expecting very soon.

She hid the babies and nursed them tenderly. Instead of cooking them she cooked some mice and when Konyeki returned and asked for his meat he was given mice. It was dark at night and as he was hungry he did not bother to look at his meat properly. He complained as he ate that it was not very tasty. His mother told him that she did not eat such horrible things and did not know how it tasted.

Konyeki complained to his father, but he too did not take notice. He trusted his wife as far as eating meat was concerned. Now Konyeki's mother took great care of the babies and she fed them with good food and her own milk and they grew very fast. She prayed to God to save her and the babies. God answered her prayers. Almost by a miracle the babies never cried, throughout all their childhood. Konyeki and his father never realized that there were other boys growing in their homestead.

When the three boys grew up they were told by Konyeki's mother that their lives were in danger and that they would have to co-operate with her to remain safe; when they were big and strong she would get them swords and spears and arrows to fight the terrible and perverted ogres. The three boys understood the circumstances their mother—as they regarded her—lived in. They spent much of their time in training how to fight with swords, and to throw spears and arrows, and when they felt confident of their skill in fighting they asked their mother to permit them to fight Konyeki and his father.

Konyeki often told his father that there were far too many footsteps in their homestead, especially in the evenings, and that he suspected that there were other people either in the homestead or coming from outside. Konyeki's father ignored all this. He thought that his son was joking. Konyeki continued to be curious and asked his mother many questions regarding the footsteps found at the homestead in the afternoons and evenings. She realized the danger of holding back the three brothers from assaulting Konyeki and his father.

Konyeki's mother got good spears, swords, and arrows for the three boys and asked them to attack one evening when Konyeki and his father returned from their daily hunting. When they were ready they waited by the gate of the homestead. Konyeki and his father returned very tired and worn out because of having killed a big buffalo in the greatest heat of the sun in the jungle. As soon as they reached the gate of the homestead Konyeki and his father were attacked and soon killed, as they were almost helpless, being too tired to fight back. Konyeki cried out to his father,

'I have always told you father, I saw footsteps in our homestead! Remember I said that my meat was not good and that mother did not cook the babies!' And as Konyeki finished saying this his neck was hacked off with a sharp sword and he and his father were burnt into ashes by the three brothers, who took their mother back to their home. They were kindly received by the villagers and when they told the story of Konyeki and his father the three brothers were put in the ranks of great warriors of the tribe and were respected throughout the tribe.

Mwithanga and the Great River Monster

ONCE upon a time a great monster lived in a big river near a village. It was a great misfortune for anyone to see the monster. He would be eaten or die of horror and fear. The monster lived under the water, and came out at night, when it would go to the villages to steal cattle and even people for its food.

One day Mwithanga went to draw water from the river. As she was about to pick up her gourd full of water and return home to cook for her family, she gazed across the water where she heard a peculiar noise, and to her horror, she saw the frightful monster coming towards her. She was terrified.

'Do not move, Mwithanga,' the monster spoke to her, 'I have not had anything to eat for some time, and I shall have to eat you.'

'Oh, please spare me,' she pleaded, 'I shall give you all the food in my homestead if you will spare my life.'

The monster agreed to go to the homestead on the day arranged between them, and feed on the food she would prepare for it.

Mwithanga returned home and quickly told her husband what had happened. Her husband agreed with her that they should cook a lot of food for the monster, and Mwithanga asked everybody in the homestead to hide away when the monster came to eat the food.

The monster came on the appointed day, and as it walked, it called out,

'Mwithanga! Mwithanga! *Ageni mekuria ki?* Mwithanga! Mwithanga! What have you got for your guest?'

When it got to her home, it ate all the food that was cooked, and then started on all the cattle, goats, sheep, raw food, and grains in the granaries of the homestead. He ate the houses, the granaries, Mwithanga, her husband, and everybody in the village, except one boy who ran right away from the village when the monster was calling Mwithanga.

The boy witnessed the tragedy of the family and villagers from a hill afar off. He was most grieved to see his family and relations swallowed by this terrible monster. He took his sword, spear, and arrows, and decided to go to the river, wait there for the monster, and fight it by the riverside.

When the monster finished eating everything that it could find, and had wrecked the whole village, it started to walk slowly back to the river. It was very tired, and by the time it got back to the riverside it was almost unable to move because of the great weight in its stomach. The boy jumped on to its head, and with his sharp sword slashed the monster's throat. The monster was helpless. It could hardly defend itself. The boy came to its side and cut open its stomach. It died, and as it died, the people of the village started coming out and said to the boy,

'Please be careful, don't cut me.' His mother, father, sisters, brothers, relations and friends came out. Next came the cattle, sheep, and goats. The people returned to their village, and free from fear of the monster, lived happily ever after.

The Land of the Spirits

ONCE upon a time in the Gikuyu country there was a man who was widely renowned for his mystical visions and prophesies. Many a time he disappeared from his bed at night, and when people inspected his hut they could not see a sign to indicate whether he had left through the door or the roof. They did this because they were curious whether he had left naturally or on his spiritual missions. Sometimes he stayed away for days, sometimes for weeks, and sometimes for months, and eventually he would return mysteriously as usual. People from the villages would come to hear the stories of the mysterious places he had visited. One of them which he told most vividly is the story of the Land of the Spirits.

'The land round me looked very much like Gikuyu country, with mountains, hills, valleys, plains, rivers and forests. Yet it was very much more beautiful and fertile, and was ever green everywhere. The rivers were of clear blue water I could see homesteads in the distance, and smoke and fire glowing inside the houses. When I walked towards the homesteads, they would be no more. I would see pots of food cooking on the firestones out in the open, and went to ask to share with the people owning them. But as I got near the pots, the delicious smelling food would disappear. As I went to touch them and examine the inside of the empty pots, they too would disappear.

'I heard voices from roadsides and homesteads. But I saw no one. The voices of girls and women coming to draw water approached me. I followed them up towards the homesteads on the hilltops. No sooner did I get there than I found them

17

elsewhere. I pleaded with the voices to talk to me. I asked them if they would offer me hospitality. But no voices answered my appeals.

'Away in the forest was smoke and the sound of people felling trees. I saw trees fall and the timber split apart. But not the people who did it. Along went bundles of wood, at an angle as if on the backs of women carrying them, going in the direction of the hills. I saw them going along and passing me.

'When I roamed in the wilderness, amid bushes and forest, there were sounds of fierce animals. I was very afraid. Elephants were trumpeting. There were sounds of rhinoceros charging. I was petrified. Yet as soon as these wild beasts should have rushed near me, they were no more.

'There were fields of beautiful bananas, and banana trees being cut. I could see bunches of bananas a little way off the ground, going in the direction of the hills. I could hear voices of men and women in conversation. At times there were cowbells ringing and cows mooing, and goats and sheep bleating. But never at any time did I see them.

'In the fields there were all sorts of crops growing. There was nothing I had seen growing in the Gikuyu that I did not see growing in this land. The scenery was magnificent, more beautiful than is generally seen. The scent of the flowers was most fragrant. Everything grew in a more perfect condition than I could ever remember seeing before. But I could not touch the flowers. And wherever I passed, the trees, rivers, homesteads, and animals all made way for me, so that I might not touch them.

'Shouts and cries came from the river. It was time for the people to meet their friends there, and take a swim. There were noises of splashing and water games, with people joking and laughing. I could see the sparkle and glint on the water as people splashed and swam about. But neither in front, nor on any side could I espy the people who were bathing.

'I was in the midst of people; yet I was starving. No one would give anything to me; and if I put out my hand to steal, the object disappeared at once. The water drank itself; the food cooked and ate itself; the fire lit and extinguished itself; the bananas ripened, peeled, and ate themselves; the trees felled and cut themselves into firewood; which in turn carried itself.

'The homesteads built and demolished themselves; voices spoke and sang to themselves; the light of the sun was beautiful, and the heat was moderate, not too hot and never cold.

'In the night it was not like the night, because there was moonlight shining as bright as the daylight, throughout. And also because the temperature was the same as during the day. Life always seemed the same whether it was night or day.

'There were many beautiful and natural flowers in the fields as well as in the bushes. I could hear the birds singing; and also the bees and other insects flying from flower to flower collecting honey: But I could not see the actual birds or insects. There was not a single sound of people, animals, birds, or insects that I had heard in Gikuyu country that I did not hear in this strange land, but I could not see these objects themselves; nor would they respond to my humble appeals.

'This was the land of spirits where no human beings could live.'

The Woman and the Bird

O NCE upon a time there was a woman who hated birds. One day she went to cut down a banana tree, and while she was cutting it down a bird kept flying near her, cheeping miserably. It was trying to stop her from felling the banana tree, because she had a nest with eggs on the tree. The woman realized this was the reason why the bird was worried, but paid no attention. As the banana tree fell down, the eggs were broken and the unborn chicks were killed. The bird was very angry, and by magic or miracle she spoke like a human and cursed the woman, warning her that she would take her revenge one day. The woman laughed contemptuously and went home, carrying her bananas.

The woman was pregnant and in a few months gave birth to a baby boy. In accordance with the custom her husband slaughtered a ram and invited their relatives and friends to the ceremonial occasion of naming the child. The custom requires that the water used in this ceremony has to be drawn from the spring by a boy and a girl. Two children were chosen to perform this task. The girl's name was Njoki and the boy's Waigwaini. They were sent to the nearest spring very early in the morning to draw water before anyone else could have gone there, as the custom required to make sure the water was clean and pure and untouched.

While these arrangements were being made the bird had known all about them and was preparing to take her revenge against the woman.

She went and perched on a tree by the spring. She had

magically beautified her feathers. To human beings she looked
the most beautiful bird that man had ever seen and to Waigwaini
and Njoki it was a great fascination and joy. They stared at the
bird, and were amazed when they heard it sing. Instead of
drawing water, they sat down and listened to the bird's songs
and watched it dance. They forgot what they had come for
and kept the people at home anxiously waiting.

Now, the father decided to send another boy to call them as
it was getting late for the ceremony. As the boy was approaching and calling loud:

'*ii Waigwaini!*'

the bird answered back and said:

> *Na kahii ugwita Waigwaini! Waigwaini!*
> *Kanyoni ndeiya!*
> *Nduikuruke na rui ruru! i ruru!*
> *Kanyoni ndeiya!*
> *Wiyonere kanyoni gaka! i gaka!*
> *Kanyoni ndeiya!*
> *Geduringa muti mbari ino*
> *neno ingi!*
> *Kanyoni ndeiya!*
> *Waigwaini tini no tini!*

> You boy calling Waigwaini, Waigwaini,
> Pretty bird,
> Wouldn't you like to come down near this spring?
> Pretty bird,
> And see for yourself this pretty bird,
> Pretty bird,
> Who sings and dances on the tree from one side
>   to the other
> Pretty bird.
> Waigwaini is sitting prettily!

So the boy went down to the spring and found Waigwaini
and Njoki watching the bird and unable to speak or move. He
too was magically hypnotized by the bird, so he sat down with
them to watch and listen to the bird's music.

The people at home got worried and sent a grown-up person in case the children were in trouble. When he approached the spring and called aloud '*I i i Waigwaini i!*' he got the same reply. When he went down to the spring to his amazement he saw the children sitting listening to the beautiful songs and watching the bird dance. No sooner had he got to the spring than he joined the children, as he was also hypnotized the moment he saw the bird.

More people were sent to fetch the little children with the ceremonial water, but they all were hypnotized in turn and sat by the spring to listen to the bird. This went on until all the people at home were drawn to the spring, including the father of the infant child, and eventually the mother had to leave the infant unattended in the house to find out the fate of those who had disappeared.

When she got to the spring she called out '*I i i Waigwaini i!*' like the others and got the same reply. She went down, and before she sat down to watch, the bird flew away in the direction of the home. They wondered what had happened and they all felt stupid. They decided to help the little children to take the water and resolved to go home to continue with the ceremony. When they arrived they were all shocked to see the same bird on top of the roof, holding the infant. At this moment the woman realized that this was the bird who had cursed her and sworn to take her revenge for the destruction of her chicks some months earlier. She at once broke into tears and prayed and begged the bird to forgive her and return her baby safely.

The men were in a dilemma. If they shot the bird with arrows or threw stones from slings they might injure the baby, so although they had more than enough weapons to fight, they were helpless. So they agreed that it was a matter for God to decide, and joined the woman in her prayers.

The bird was kind and generous and asked the woman to apologize and to promise that she would be kind to birds and animals and to appreciate that the chicks she killed were as dear and precious as her own baby. The woman promised fervently that she would, and the bird brought the baby safely down to her. Then the beautiful bird flew high and disappeared into the horizon. The naming ceremony was continued and the family lived happily ever after.

The Baboons and the Village Women

A LONG time ago there was a village near the forests of the Nyandarwa* mountains. The villagers were mainly far- mers, owning cattle, goats, and sheep. They liked this area very much because it was always green and had a lot of grass for their animals. The men spent most of their time with the animals in the field while the women cultivated their shambas and cooked for their families.

The women organized themselves in communal groups and worked their shambas in rotation: that is, one day they would work on one shamba and the next day on another shamba until they had completed the round. It worked out very easily for them because they usually finished hoeing or ploughing one shamba in a day. They also harvested the crop during harvest- ing season in the same manner. While this work was going on the men were far away in the grazing fields, herding the animals.

One day the women found that their crop was being stolen by the baboons who came from the neighbouring forests. They stole maize when it was young and delicate; they completely ruined bananas, pumpkins, and young calabash which the women grew for making gourds for drawing water from the river, and in which the men brewed their beer. The women appealed to their menfolk to shoot the baboons and stop them ruining their crops. The men also were very much concerned about all the damage.

Traps were set all over the forests, and many baboons and

* Aberdare Hills.

monkeys were caught and killed. Hunting parties were also organized by the men and they raided and killed many baboons in the forests. The whole monkey race was nearly exterminated by the fierce poisoned arrows, the spears, the traps, and starvation, as now all the shambas, were guarded by men by night while women worked and guarded them by day. So those baboons who survived the raids and the traps convened a meeting of their kind to find a way out, by making peace with the villagers and living in peace. The baboons resolved to stop stealing and resort to begging for their food from the villagers. They agreed to learn nice games and songs which they would perform to entertain the villagers so that they could earn their food. Acrobatic games were among those the baboons thought best, because apart from entertaining the villagers it was a form of defence in case the men should attack with their fierce arrows. It was considered that an acrobat would duck easily and swiftly and escape being shot. Yes, this was a good idea and they were all happy about it.

When the rehearsals were finished and they felt confident, the baboons came and started singing near the edge of the fields. They sang such beautiful songs that they attracted the attention of the women who worked in the shambas. At first the women wanted to call for the men to come and fight the baboons, but one of the baboons who appeared to be the leader came forward and, speaking in a human voice, he said, 'We have come here to inform you that we have resolved not to steal your crops any more, and to let you know that we want to live as friends and good neighbours; please ask your menfolk not to kill us any more.' When he finished saying this, the other baboons cheered and played their best tunes, while the acrobats performed their most amazing feats. The women were overcome with astonishment. Then the leader of the baboons came forward again and said, 'Friends, we are glad that you have enjoyed our performance. We have children in our homes to look after, but as we have decided not to steal from you any more, we must beg you to give us your waste and bad bananas, maize, and fruit, so that we can feed our starving little ones.'

The women murmured among themselves and agreed to give the baboons some fruit. Whenever the baboons were given food they would all disappear into the forest singing:

Mutana wa wakahare, e-heee!	Squirrel's friend, e-heee!
Niki kiu kiri thunu?	Why does your bottom look
Ni hau!	like that?
	That is all.

Ni muigua wandarurire, e-heee!	The thorn wounded me, e-heee!
Tukiria ndare mutitu;	While eating red berries in
Ni hau!	the forest;
	That is all.

Na kai mwariaga inyuothe, e-heee?	Then you were all eating them, e-heee?
Na kanini na kanene?	The kids and the grown-ups?
Ni hau!	That is all.

Mucokeri wa uhoro ucio, e-heee!	What you've said should not be repeated, e-heee!
Arigua mutitu korogoco!	Lest you hear so much com-
Ni hau!	motion in the forest!
	That is all.

And on this note the baboons stopped singing and quietly returned to their homes in the forest; then they fed their children with the food given to them by the village women.

The women returned to their homes, and told the story of the songs and dances of the talking baboons to their children. The baboons went on coming to entertain the women, and one day the men decided to come and watch too. When the men saw this performance they thought it was caused by the bad spirits, as they could not believe that animals could talk. So the men went to consult the witch-doctors and seers to find out why the baboons came to entertain their wives. The witch-doctors could not find the reason.

One day the baboons came to play for the women as usual. One woman had tried to persuade the others not to continue giving their food to the baboons as there were far too many to be satisfied. They did not listen to her, but the woman decided to withold her own contribution. The baboons learnt of her unkind attitude. They decided to punish this woman who was trying to persuade the others to deny them food. While the woman was working in her garden alone she had kept her infant baby in a cot somewhere in the garden, and the baby was sleeping soundly when the leader of the baboons came quietly and secretly, stole the baby, and carried it on to a tree near by. The other baboons were up there on the tree, and at once they all started their usual acrobatic dance. They played with the baby and the baby cried. When its mother looked, she was shocked to see her baby in the hands of the baboons on the tree. The baboons threw the baby to one another like a ball. They threw the baby from one baboon to another, from one tree to another, and from one branch to another. This horrified the baby's mother, who cried and pleaded with the baboons to deliver her baby up to her, and promised to provide as many pumpkins as the baboons would like to have.

The baboons stopped teasing the woman, and their leader spoke to her, and asked her to bring the pumpkins under the tree and then go far away. The baboons would collect the ransom for the baby, and then lay it under the tree. The woman collected all the pumpkins from the garden, and set them under the tree to ransom her baby from the angry baboons. When she had done this, she went far away as instructed by the leader of the baboons.

The rest of the baboons came down and carried the pumpkins away into the forest, singing '*Mutana wa wakahare*' and their leader brought the baby down and laid it where he had promised. The woman picked up the baby and ran home to tell her husband all about her frightening experience.

When the villagers learned of the savage act of the baboons, they and their leaders all agreed to continue their campaign against the baboons, and keep them as far away from their homes and fields as possible; the women were warned not to listen to the deceptive baboons any more. Since then the baboons and monkeys have lived on trees in the forests, and they still perform their acrobatic dances, both as a strategic defence and in the hope that they will one day succeed in persuading men to accept them as entertainers and earn the nuts, bananas, pumpkins, and other delicacies grown by men, which the monkeykind so much like to eat.

The Story of Hyena and Squirrel

A LONG time ago, hyena and squirrel were great friends and lived in the same homestead. They were very wealthy. They had many goats, cattle, and sheep. Both of them were good herdsmen, and took great care of their animals. They grazed them in turn; that is, the hyena would be in the homestead looking after domestic affairs there for so many days, while the squirrel grazed the animals for so many days, and so on.

One day the hyena began to think how he might own all the animals, and kill the squirrel. Often when they were in the field together grazing their animals, he would suggest to the squirrel that they should go for a swim in the river. He always hoped to drown the squirrel, but realizing this, the squirrel always avoided swimming near the hyena. So the hyena tried all sorts of tricks, but his friend was too smart to fall into any of his traps.

When the squirrel realized that the hyena really meant to kill him, he decided to retaliate. One day, the hyena was in the field grazing their animals, while the squirrel was left to look after the housework and cook. Squirrel cooked a very nice dish of meat, and the fragrant delicious food could be smelled from afar. He also burnt a small stone red-hot, which he wanted to use to kill the hyena. At sunset, when the herdsmen returned their animals to their homesteads, the squirrel was expecting his friend to bring back their animals and put them in the sheds. Usually the hyena was very hungry at the end of a day's work and he ate whatever he was given very gluttonously. He would complain bitterly if the food was not ready for him when he returned home.

Now one could hear the bells of the bulls and goats coming nearer and nearer. The hyena was coming home, very hungry as usual. When he was only a few yards away, the cunning squirrel rolled the red-hot stone in meat and fat, and made a nice roll of delicious meat round it. It looked like a kind of meat ball, and its fragrance made the hyena's mouth water. The hot stone was burning the meat and fat and it produced such a nice smell that one could smell it from a long way away.

At the gate of the homestead, the hyena shouted and asked if there was something nice for him to eat. He said that he was very hungry and threatened to eat the squirrel if there was not enough food for him. This did not worry the squirrel. He called out that he had cooked special food that evening and that the hyena would be sure to enjoy it. But this assurance did not seem to please the hyena, who was more interested in killing the squirrel than in having nice food. He advanced towards the squirrel very angrily, when the latter said to him,

'Eh, my dear friend Hyena, look I have made very special and nice food for you. Can't you smell it?'

'Yes,' replied the hyena, 'I can smell it, but is it enough? I am tired and hungry after spending the whole day looking after these animals of yours. If there isn't enough food, I shall have to eat *you* for supper tonight.'

'Oh no, my friend Hyena,' replied the squirrel; 'there is more food than you can eat.' And at this point he picked up the roll of meat with the red-hot stone inside, and said,

'Open your mouth, my friend Hyena, and taste this special piece of meat. Swallow it at once while I serve you yet a larger dish of meat.'

The hyena opened his mouth without hesitation or suspicion, and the squirrel threw the roll of meat right into his mouth; as it was too small to chew, he swallowed it at once. It was delicious and tasty as it went down, but a few seconds after he had

swallowed it, the red-hot stone produced so much heat in the
hyena's stomach that it killed him instantly. So the squirrel
was left in peace. He acquired the possession of all the animals
and all the land, and lived happily ever after.

Hare and the Well in the Jungle

A LONG time ago there was a great drought which dried all the rivers and lakes, and threatened all the animals in the jungle with thirst, hunger, and starvation. Lion the king, summoned all the animals and commanded that they should dig a big well from which they would drink and irrigate the vegetation in the forest to maintain enough food for the kingdom during the drought.

It was agreed by all the animals that they dig the well as commanded by his majesty, and on the day appointed the animals came to dig the well. Everyone was present except the hare, who decided to stay away. When the well was completed, King Lion and his subjects agreed to pass a law outlawing the hare and forbidding him to drink from the well or to feed on the grass that was grown from the irrigation.

The hare learnt of this law which outlawed him, but was not in the least disturbed. He knew that most of the other animals were stupid, and he the cleverest of them all. So he went secretly and drank water without being seen.

The lion had arranged that the animals would guard the well in turn. One day when the old hyena was on guard, the hare came and dived into the well to bathe and drink. The hyena saw him and caught him. He pushed the hare under the water, intending to drown him and take his carcass to King Lion. The hyena would win the honour of a good guard and respect of other animals in the jungle kingdom. But unaware of this fact, the hare always came with a long straw, one end of which he put in his mouth while the other was left above the water, properly secured at the edge of the well, while he swam and dived below. So he was not at all affected by the hyena's pressure.

When the hyena thought that the little animal was suffocated and drowned, he brought him to the surface, and to his surprise, found that it was still alive. They were both very wet and shivering from the cold.

The hyena wanted to kill the hare there and then, and take his dead body to the lion.

'Oh, Hyena, don't kill me before I am tried by the court,' cried the hare; 'it is against the law to kill me before King Lion has seen me and tried me himself. He would think that you are taking the law into your hands, and might even think that you are usurping his powers and want to take over his kingdom!'

Hyena realized the danger of taking the law into his own hands, and convinced of the importance of producing Hare before the court alive said,

'All right, I shall take you before King Lion and you shall have your trial, but I can assure you that you shall die before sunset, you rascal!'

'Yes, but, yes,' the hare replied, 'but I am dying now. See how I am shivering of cold. I am dying of cold. Please, Hyena, get some dry banana strings* and tie me up, and then lay me in the sun somewhere so that I may dry and recover from this dreadful cold. If I die of cold, Lion might think you killed me before he tried me.' Again the hyena was so convinced that he complied with the hare's request.

When the hare was tied up and left in the sun to dry, he slowly cut the strings, which were already beginning to break by themselves in the heat of the sun. Meanwhile the hyena, quite sure that Hare was helpless, dozed off in the great heat of the sun, after his swim in the well. He was not really much bothered and did not at all suspect that the hare would escape.

* Banana strings are very delicate and break easily, especially in the sun.

Quietly the hare picked up a heavy stone, smashed the hyena on the head, and ran away to leave him dying.

Away into the forest he ran, and soon rain came, and streams returned, and the vegetation grew. Hare never came to the well again, and lived happily ever after.

How the Wild Turkey got its Spots

A LONG time ago, Nganga, the wild turkey, was pitch black in colour, and easily distinguished from other birds. Lion, the king of the jungle, did not want to catch Nganga, because he regarded her as a bird of bad spirits.

One day, Lion wanted to kill a cow and eat her. This cow had very sharp strong horns and was able to defend herself on many occasions when attacked by other beasts. Lion charged the cow, and was about to overcome her, when suddenly Nganga came quickly, and rushing between the two animals, blew up a lot of dust, which made a large cloud and almost blinded the lion. While he was in confusion with pain in his eyes from the dust, the cow escaped without being seen.

When King Lion recovered from the pain in his eyes, he tried to look for the trail of the cow, but Nganga had blown so much dust that when it settled down it covered all the old marks on the ground. There was not a sign of any disturbance, not even of the great fight between the cow and the lion. This annoyed him very much, but since he had always regarded Nganga as a bird of bad spirits, he gave up the idea of eating beef that day.

Another day, King Lion met the cow while going to the stream to drink. Another fight started, and again Nganga came suddenly and blew a lot of dust between the two animals, blinding and confusing Lion once again.

Again the cow escaped. Lion decided to catch Nganga and kill her. He waited at a place where Nganga had her chicks, and tried to catch her, but she was too swift as she flew backward and forward, biting the lion on the back with her sharp beak. There was a terrific noise from the cry of Nganga and the chicks, and from the fierce roaring of the angry lion. Nganga was getting exhausted, and ran towards the river for a quick drink, before continuing the fight. King Lion followed her towards the river; Nganga, flying fast, got to the river, had a quick drink, and as she was returning to carry on the fight she saw the cow whom she had twice saved from the lion. The cow called to Nganga, and wetted her tail brush with milk, which she sprinkled all over Nganga's body. When King Lion came running down the hill, he saw a beautiful white spotted bird, and asked her,

'Did you see Nganga come down this way?'

'Yes,' Nganga replied, 'she has just passed here a few moments ago, and she is heading towards that forest across the river.' The lion rushed on towards the forest to catch Nganga. The cow, who was hiding somewhere near by, came out and thanked Nganga for saving her before.

'Don't thank me, my friend,' Nganga replied politely, 'you have saved many more lives than mine, and my chicks too. I should thank you myself.'

The cow then asked Nganga to bring her chicks so that they could also be sprinkled with milk and have white spots like their mother in case the lion returned.

That is how the wild turkey acquired its spots.

The Great Famine and the Law of the Jungle

ONCE upon a time, the kingdom of the jungle was harassed by a great drought which dried up all the rivers, streams, and water-holes, and animals were dying in great numbers because of hunger and thirst. Lion, the king of the jungle, summoned all his senior ministers, such as the elephant, tiger, leopard, rhino, buffalo, hippopotamus and all the other distinguished gentlemen of the kingdom, to discuss ways and means of saving it from destruction by the famine.

Most of the meat-eaters such as hyena, leopard, crocodile, and others feasted on the meat of those who died and were really little concerned about the dangers of the drought because they had more to eat than during rainy seasons, but Lion the king was greatly alarmed because he knew only too well that after all the vegetarian members of his kingdom had died of hunger even the meat-eaters would have to die when there was no more meat for them. There was great anxiety and confusion in the whole kingdom and when the council of ministers met, they decided to emigrate to another region in the mountainous highlands of Kenya which was not so badly affected by the drought, because of constant rain attracted by the mountains throughout the year, and the numerous streams around the mountains. This region was always green and was inhabited by great farmers who were natural and perpetual enemies of the jungle kingdom, but as the lion had no choice but to lead his subjects, he and his ministers passed a law compelling all of them to travel together to find a new home.

When the news was spread, many were reluctant to join such a safari, as they did not feel safe to travel in such a company full of meat-eaters, fearing that they might be eaten before they even got to their destination. But they had no say because their king had made them promise under oath to emigrate to the higher region near the mountains where they would find enough food to live on. They were also ordered to walk quickly and fast in a procession across the dry jungle without a stop, and that anyone who stopped without a valid and reasonable excuse would have to be eaten. This law did not worry the meat-eaters, because they were in good health, and strong enough to walk as they had been eating the meat of those who had died of starvation, but for the vegetarians this was almost impossible, because they were weak already, having had very little grass to eat and vegetables having long since died. However, they had to comply with the law whether they liked it or not. The king had ordered them to walk, and they had to walk.

So they started off, fully understanding the consequences of stopping on the way. They did not go very far before many of them collapsed because of the heat of the sun and hunger and thirst. The meat-eaters then ate those who collapsed or stopped. This went on until all the weaker members of their society were liquidated and only strong ones were left, except Hare, who endured the difficulties, because he was clever enough to find his food by going under the rocks and in little holes, where he found some water and mushroom and a little grass on which he fed while the others ate those who died.

As soon as they had finished eating the dead ones, they continued their journey without stopping, in accordance with the law, and as there were not many collapsing now, they did not have much to eat and they seemed to be very anxious to see anyone break the law, so that they could catch him and eat him as the law had provided.

The hyena grew weak and unable to walk any further; he stopped.

'Hyena has stopped,' said the other animals.

'Oh, no! I was thinking,' said the hyena.

'What were you thinking about?' asked the lion. And unable to answer this question, the hyena was caught and devoured by the others.

They continued on their journey and many of the jungle lords like the elephant, rhino, hippopotamus, and others, broke this law by stopping and they were consequently killed and eaten in turn. Hare was determined to survive although he stopped several times. When he stopped first and others wanted to eat him, if he did not have a valid or reasonable excuse, he said he was thinking.

'What were you thinking about?' asked the lion.

'Where do old clothes go, when people buy new clothes?' asked the hare. The lion and others wondered if they knew the answer to this question, and they all agreed that they did not know it, and that the hare was really thinking, and thus had not really broken the law.

They continued their journey; many others, trying to use Hare's technique, failed to give satisfactory reasons for their stopping, and got eaten up. The hare would stop any time he felt too tired to walk, and would always give some reason for his stopping. At one time he wondered why some stones were large and very thick, whereas some were small like pebbles.

'Did they not have the same amount of rain and food like the larger stones?' he asked. And to this the others were unable to give an answer. He went on stopping from time to time and he always got away with it. But when all the other animals had been eaten up by the lion, the hare got very much concerned about his own safety, because he knew now it was not a matter of law or wit, but a matter of survival of the fittest. Lion had to have his next meal, and there was no other to provide it but the hare himself.

So he had to think quickly of ways and means of escaping the danger. He noticed a great mass of rocks ahead of them, and soon he could see spaces here and there, where he could get through and under, to the other side. Some of the spaces seemed large enough for the lion to go through as well. Hare found one space which narrowed as it went through the rocks, but was still large enough for him to go through to the other side. He decided to deceive the lion, and get him to pass through those spaces so that he should get stuck. He deliberately stopped, and answering the lion's questions he said that he wanted to play a game of hide-and-seek by passing through those holes in the rocks. Lion was very agreeable as he thought that he would catch the hare and eat him.

The hare started running and jumping into the holes, and coming out the other end, and the lion chased after him, and got through those holes which were large enough for him to go through, omitting the small ones. Eventually the hare jumped into the large hole which narrowed towards the other end, and unaware of this, the lion came running very fast, got into it, and stuck there. When he tried to go backward he was prevented by the spikelike stones which faced the other direction. The hare crawled out the other end and mockingly said,

'Mr Lion has stopped! He must be eaten.' The lion was unable to give any reason, and the hare went round about, came up to the lion's back, squeezed under his haunches, and started biting his stomach.

'My dear friend, Mr Hare, please come in front and start eating me from the head,' pleaded the lion.

'Oh! No! Your majesty, I feel ashamed of myself that I have to fulfil the obligation of the law, and I feel that I should not let you see me eating you, my lord. I shall eat you from the back,' replied the hare.

With this remark, he tore open the lion's stomach, and the lion died at once. The hare quickly got out of the hole, and continued his journey slowly to the fertile highlands near Mount Kenya, where he lived happily ever after.

The Story of Mwathi and his Creditors

I

A LONG time ago there lived near Nyandarwa Forest a small man whose name was Mwathi. He was an orphan and had very little education as his parents died when he was only a few months old. Although he owned a very large and fertile piece of land he did not know how to cultivate it properly. He made his livelihood by hunting but he could also entice even the most savage animals and make friends with them.

Mwathi's neighbours had developed their land on which they grew all kinds of tropical crops and mostly sweet potatoes. They also kept cattle, goats, and sheep. Mwathi wanted to have some goats of his own but he did not know the art of animal husbandry as well as he knew the wild animals. One day he decided to cultivate a small piece of his land and plant some sweet potatoes. As his land was very fertile his crops grew faster and better than that of his neighbours. He himself having no goats to feed with the green part of his crop, he sold it to his neighbour who gave him a kid in exchange. He was very happy to possess a goat for the first time in his life.

He took the kid home and put it into a granary. He fed it with sweet potatoes, grain, and anything sweet that he could find. He cultivated a larger piece of his land and grew more, which he used as fodder to feed his goat. Apart from his usual occupation of hunting he devoted a great part of his time to

looking after the goat. It grew very large and fat, so much so
that it filled the whole space of the small granary and could not
come out. Mwathi was getting worried about the safety of his
animal and was wondering whether to continue feeding it, or
whether to stop and starve it so that it could get small enough
to be brought out. He realized that if he starved the animal it
would die and therefore he decided to break open the granary
immediately. He tried this and the animal was very frightened
and bleated in terror. He felt that he was not very clever in
doing it and therefore he set out to the villages and highways
to look for someone who would bring out his beloved animal
from the granary peacefully and safely.

He met many people and sought their help. The lion was one
of those who were very keen to offer their help.

'My friend, Mwathi, why are you crying so much?' he asked.

'I am worried about my goat which is stuck in my granary.
Do you know how to befriend goats?' asked Mwathi.

'Yes, my friend I think I can help you to bring it out,' said
the lion.

'I need your help very badly, but are you sure you wouldn't
frighten my beloved goat?' asked Mwathi.

'Oh no! you can rely on me. I am an expert in animal husbandry, and your goat will like me when I speak to him,' said
the lion.

'Would you like to whistle and let me see if my goat will
like you?' asked Mwathi. The lion struggled to whistle with
his mouth, but he could not do it, so instead he roared and told
Mwathi that his goat would like that. Mwathi thanked him and
courteously told him that he would come to him on the
following day if his help was needed. Of course, Mwathi did
not like him but he did not want to be impolite to the King of
the Jungle who could have used his prerogative and seen that he
attended Mwathi's goat whether his voice was liked or not.

In his efforts Mwathi met many distinguished citizens of the
Jungle Kingdom such as the rhino, elephant, buffalo, gorilla,
hyena, and many others, all of whom disappointed him because
of their failure to speak in a voice familiar and pleasing to his

goat. He almost gave up in despair when he met the leopard, who qualified because he could speak and whistle like a good shepherd. Without wasting time, Mwathi invited him to come and free his goat from the granary.

When they got there, the leopard squeezed himself gently and carefully through the small entrance and got inside. He got hold of the goat by the throat, killed it, and drank all the blood out of it. Mwathi heard a little of the struggle and inquiring into the progress of the leopard, he was assured that the goat was going to come out almost immediately. And the leopard fulfilled this promise, for as soon as he sucked the blood out of the whole animal he forced the carcass out of the entrance and threw it onto the ground before Mwathi. At first Mwathi thought the animal was alive but examining it closely he realized that it was dead. He cried bitterly but it was hopeless and the leopard, told him that it was useless to cry as there was nothing he could do to bring the goat out other than to drink its blood in order to diminish it in size so that it would go past the entrance. Mwathi seemed to be convinced by this explanation but he still feared that the leopard might rob him of the meat as well. He had to think quickly how to overcome his trickery. Physically he could not fight him, so he could only defeat him by outwitting him.

The leopard, showing his teeth and claws, reassured his friend that he was ready to help skin the animal. He suggested that they should go somewhere in the forest and make a fire under the shade of a tree, roast the meat, and have a nice feast. He thought it was not very wise to roast meat at Mwathi's home since there would be much interference from uninvited neighbours. Mwathi agreed and they carried the goat into the forest under a big tree by the side of the river which ran through the forest. The leopard cut up the meat into pieces ready for roasting and he requested his friend Mwathi to fetch the fire from a neighbouring village.

He went to fetch the fire but he put it out with water as he came back, and reported to the leopard that some rude and nasty girls who were playing at the riverside had beaten him up and put out the fire. The leopard was angry and ordered him to go back and get some more fire. Mwathi obediently went to fetch some more fire, did the same thing as before and reported to the leopard that the girls would not let him pass with the fire. He was sent a third time and the same thing happened. He asked the leopard to go to fetch the fire as the girls might respect him better. So the furious leopard went away to fetch the fire. First he stopped at the place where the girls were playing and he started quarrelling with them. They did not understand what he was talking about, but as the leopard did not want to waste much time he continued his journey to fetch fire so that he could come and roast meat, and feast.

The moment the leopard left, Mwathi selected a very tall, thick tree and carried all the meat up to the top. He was sure the leopard would not care to climb such a tree and would therefore give up any idea of feasting on his meat. The leopard came back with fire, but to his disappointment there was neither meat nor Mwathi to be found. He gazed around in search of his friend. He tried to trail the footprints and he smelled in all directions and could not make up his mind where his friend had gone with the meat. He suddenly looked up the tree and there at the top he saw his friend with his meat properly secured on the tree. He called out to him and said,

'Oh! my dear friend, won't you give me a piece of meat for the work I have done for you?'

'No, I'm sorry, you killed my goat so that you could have some meat. There is no meat for you here,' replied Mwathi.

'Not even a piece of bone, please?' asked the leopard.

'No! not even a bone, you dirty trickster! I shall give you nothing, absolutely nothing,' replied Mwathi.

At this point the leopard gave up, but warned Mwathi that one day he would catch him at the spring in the valley and take his revenge for such humiliation. Mwathi did not pay any attention to this threat, and let the leopard go without any further argument.

II

At a near-by valley there was a spring which formed a little pool of beautifully fresh water. Naturally most animals and people preferred to drink from this spring rather than from the big river which was muddy, and worst of all, infested with crocodiles and hippos. The leopard was more than certain that Mwathi would soon be coming to the pool for a drink. He therefore decided to fence the pool, leaving one entrance, so that he could check on all those who came to drink, hoping that he would catch Mwathi. He asked his two sons to guard the pool by day and he guarded it by night. Mwathi knew of this arrangement as he constantly spied on the leopard's movements.

Whenever he got thirsty and badly needed a drink of water, Mwathi would disguise himself by means of camouflage. One day he would wear beautiful flowers all over his body, so that when he was moving he looked like a waving bush of flowers. When he got to the pool he would quickly jump into the water, drink to his heart's content and draw some into his calabash to take home with him. When the leopard's sons saw him they would just laugh at the sight of a mobile bush of flowers. They would continue with their play as usual without bothering to find out whether that was a real bush of flowers or Mwathi in disguise.

When the leopard came at sunset to relieve his sons he would ask them to tell him of all the people who had come for a drink that day. Then they would mention all the names of all the animals and people as far as they could remember. They would also report the peculiar bush of flowers which came to drink.

The leopard angrily asked his sons why they did not try to find out who it really was, as possibly it could have been Mwathi disguised in flowers. He ordered them to catch the mobile bush of flowers when it came next.

When Mwathi had exhausted his water in the calabash and wished to come for another drink and another fill, he would prepare a different garment for himself. Sometimes he would collect feathers and make himself a beautiful coat. When he put it on he looked like a large and strange bird, and when he went to the pool the two leopard boys would not bother him. At other times he would make a dress from porcupine quills, or leaves of various plants, so that he looked different each time he went for a drink. He confused the two leopard boys completely and they did not know how to carry out their father's order, because each day they were told to catch the mobile bush of flowers if it came again, or the mobile green leaves if it came again, and so on, whereas Mwathi always came in different guises and never repeated himself. By this time the leopard had had enough. He decided to relieve his children of this duty and took the responsibility to guard the pool by day and in the early hours of the evening. He resolved to catch any peculiar object that would come to the pool.

Mwathi did not know of this new arrangement, and the following day he came down to the pool disguised in dry banana leaves. When he jumped into the water the leopard jumped on to him immediately and tore his garment into pieces.

'Look; I told you I would catch you here one day. You are now going to pay for what you did to me,' he said, and in this instant he had bound Mwathi with strips taken from the trunks of banana trees, which he had kept ready for this purpose. He took his parcel home and gave it to his mother and asked her to cook it in hot boiling water without opening it first. The leopard's mother was very curious because she had always opened such bundles before, when her son had come back from hunting. The leopard went away and was to return in the late afternoon to have his dinner. From curiosity his mother opened the parcel before dipping it into the hot boiling water, when suddenly Mwathi jumped clear. In the moment of confusion he grabbed the leopard's mother, gagged, and bound her. He hid her somewhere in the hut. He went out into the bush near by and caught a big creature which was about the same size as himself and resembled a mouse. He bound it in the same wrappers and dipped it into the hot boiling water. He dressed himself in the clothes of the leopard's mother and went to her bed, which was screened off from the fire-place.

The leopard returned at sunset as expected, and entering into his mother's hut asked her if his food was ready. Mwathi disguising his voice to sound like the mother, told him that she was not feeling well and that he should open the pot on the fire and see if it was ready. The leopard opened the pot, took out the bound meat, and sat down to eat it. As the hut was dark inside with very little light from the fire he could not see his food clearly, but he was hungry and he did not mind much about light. Gluttonously he tore the animal into pieces and ate it quickly. When he had almost finished he began to taste something unusual, and grumbled at his mother why it tasted like that.

'Why do you ask me such silly questions, my son? You know that I don't eat those queer creatures you catch in the forest,' said Mwathi, pretending to be the mother. Apologizing to his mother, the leopard continued to eat his meal, when suddenly somebody dashed past swiftly out of the hut. Standing outside the hut Mwathi mocked the leopard for eating a mouse thinking he was eating his enemy, Mwathi. He also told him to release his mother, who was bound near the bed. The leopard jumped out quickly to catch Mwathi but Mwathi had disappeared. He returned into the hut and released his mother who reported what had happened. The leopard was very angry with his mother and warned her to be careful in future. He told her that he would bring Mwathi back, and went out in search of him.

For some days the leopard kept watch on the pool and the neighbouring rivers, the little paths, and the highways, hoping to catch Mwathi. One day Mwathi was passing somewhere near the pool and as he noticed that the leopard's sons were playing away from the pool he decided to have a quick drink before he continued his journey. But he was surprised by the leopard, who was hiding somewhere by the clumsy hedging fence of boughs around the pool. This time the leopard was determined

48

to kill Mwathi there and then and take him home to his mother as a carcass, to be cooked. He seized him and told him that this time he would not be able to escape and that he was going to pay for his debt in earnest.

Mwathi was full of fear for his life, and trembling, begged the leopard to spare him and asked him to name anything that he would accept as a compensation. The leopard thinking that Mwathi would not be able to do it, told him that he would spare his life if he could catch the monkeys in the forest and bring them to him the following day.

At first Mwathi thought this was too much, as he was not clever in the art of jumping on the trees from branch to branch and from tree to tree, as the monkeys did. He thought for a moment and requested the leopard to name something else.

'You wanted me to name anything I would accept as a compensation. I demand that you fulfil your promise or I shall kill you,' said the leopard.

Mwathi had no choice but to go for the monkeys, so he accepted the condition and promised that he would bring the monkeys the following morning. But he asked the leopard to agree to a little plan which he was going to make.

'Look, there is a big porcupine hole over there which is large enough to contain all the monkeys in this forest,' said Mwathi. 'The hole is unoccupied and exceptionally large and at the end it is like a big hall; there you can wait and kill the monkeys one by one as I send them down,' he continued.

The leopard agreed. As he was setting Mwathi free he emphasized that this was his last chance to pay off his debt and that if he failed he, the leopard, would catch and kill Mwathi without mercy. Mwathi thanked him and said that he would keep his promise.

III

Mwathi went straight into the forest to look for the monkeys; he carried a lot of nuts with him and when he found the monkeys he gave them some of the nuts. He cracked some himself with his strong good teeth. As there were no nuts in that forest monkeys had not learnt how to crack hard nutshells. They usually preferred to eat melons, which they stole from the farms near by. This made their teeth very delicate. When they failed to crack the nuts, Mwathi laughed at them. Sitting down majestically he cracked his nuts, ate some, and gave some to the monkeys. When they asked him how he got such strong teeth he told them that he had undergone the customary initiation ceremony of circumcision which gave strength to his teeth. They all laughed and asked him how they could go through it in order to strengthen their teeth. He told them that he was quite willing to take them to a special doctor who would circumcise them painlessly. They were very enthusiastic and wanted it to happen as quickly as possible, because this would not only strengthen their teeth but promote them into the higher rank of their jungle society.

Mwathi persuaded them to come with him early next morning to go to the good specialist, who would not demand any fees for this job as he believed in equality and justice for all the members of the jungle, and who particularly wanted to emancipate the monkeys from living in the fear of other, stronger animals who roamed in the forest and caused the monkeys to live perpetually in fear on top of trees. They were very happy to hear this and agreed to go with him to the porcupine hole the following morning.

When they congregated at the porcupine hole the next morning, Mwathi asked them to go in one by one. They followed his instructions, and one after the other they went down in a long queue. The leopard was very busy killing them one after the other as they came in and Mwathi was busy at the top directing them how to go. At the end of the queue there was one little pregnant monkey who came slowly, limping, looking very suspicious, and unwilling to obey Mwathi's instructions.

'Why is it that no one has come back from the hole?' asked this little monkey.

'You will all come out when you have gone through the ceremony in accordance with the rites and laws of our custom,' answered Mwathi. But the little monkey was still unwilling to go down as she felt a bit unsafe in her pregnant condition. She was particularly suspicious because female monkeys should not have gone down for circumcision, but Mwathi assured her that they went down as observers and to commiserate with their menfolk in any pain they had suffered. She did not accept this explanation either, and when Mwathi attempted to force her to go down, she escaped and ran for her life. He tried to chase her, but decided to let her go free because the leopard had had more than enough in any case.

IV

Mwathi went back to the porcupine hole, called out to the leopard, and told him that he had done his part of the bargain and wanted to know if the leopard was satisfied. With blood all over his coat and sweating profusely because of the great slaughter of the poor monkeys, the leopard came out to thank Mwathi and to wish him great success in his future life, promising that he would never harm him.

The pregnant monkey went deep into the forest and hid herself in the thickest part and made sure Mwathi could not find her. She was almost certain that the monkeys had perished in the porcupine hole. She was furiously angry with Mwathi and swore to revenge the other monkeys when she was able to.

After a few weeks she gave birth to two baby boys. She was very happy and felt that they would fight Mwathi when they grew up. She took great care of them. She fed them on all the fruits and vegetables that grew wild in the forest and as there were no other monkeys in the whole of the forest, monkey-food was in abundance.

The babies quickly grew strong. When they learned how to speak and began to understand the life of the jungle, they wondered why they and their mother were the only type of their kind in the whole forest. They troubled their mother with this question constantly and her reply was always that they should wait until they were bigger and stronger.

When they felt that they were big enough they asked their mother to explain to them why they were the only animals of their sort, whereas other species in the forest were numerous and whose children were happy to play together. The mother told them to find spears, swords, and arrows and then she would tell them why, if they would go and fight the enemy of their people.

The young monkeys quickly went to buy these weapons from a neighbouring blacksmith who lived in his smithy at the edge of the forest. When they came back they begged their mother to reveal the secret which she had withheld from them for so long.

'You see, my children, that little hut beyond that valley? The man who lives there deceived all the monkeys in this forest! He made them enter that big porcupine hole which lies on the west side of the forest, and they all perished in there except me. At that time I was carrying you in my stomach and when I suspected that the hole was not a safe place to enter, I refused to obey the instructions of that bad man and ran away and hid myself in the thickest forest. If you think you are strong and brave, then go and fight that man,' said the mother of the monkeys.

When they heard this they were indeed astonished. They promised their mother that they would go to fight that man next morning before he left his hut.

The following morning the two young monkeys, carrying their new weapons, walked into Mwathi's hut. And courteously Mwathi welcomed them, gave them some sweet melon for their breakfast, and inquired into their business. They told him of the terrible story they heard from their mother. He said that it was peculiar that they should believe stories of things that had taken place before they were born and moreover their only witness was their mother, and that they intended to prosecute him on such fickle and slender evidence. While they were agreeing on points of technicality he gave them some more of his melons which they seemed to enjoy so much. They even wondered if he had ever been as cruel as they had been made to believe. They had not eaten melon before and they asked him where they could obtain them. He told them that he would show them a field which was full of melons but on two conditions. First that they would drop that silly accusation and second that they would collect the melons themselves while he engaged the girls who worked in the field by singing to them and showing them beautiful dances. They agreed to do this. He then asked them to come with him next day about noon.

The following day they came to Mwathi as promised. They told him that they had pacified their mother, who also appreciated his kindness after tasting the melon that they took home to her. Mwathi put on his most beautiful dancing costume, with his flute and his little rattling bells around his ankles, and off they went to the melon field. He asked the monkeys to wait by the edge of the field and as soon as he started dancing for the girls, they should get into the field, eat and carry as many melons as they could.

When he got to the position where the girls were sitting and chatting he started his most enticing dances, blowing his flute, jingling his little bells around his ankles, and swinging the beautiful ostrich feathers on his head. He completely stupefied the girls and made all of them come around him. The monkeys ate the melons and carried a lot into the forest and when Mwathi was sure this had happened, he slowly went away towards his home, dancing. The girls followed him for some time and he told them they had to go back and look after their melons lest the monkeys in the forest should come and steal them. The girls at once realized that they had some responsibility and they quickly went back but only to find that so much damage was done. They did not know whether to blame Mwathi for this damage or to blame themselves. Some of them were angry with Mwathi and swore to punish him if they ever met him again.

V

One day, unaware of the girls' anger and desire for revenge, Mwathi walked into the field again intending to buy a melon for himself, when the girls surrounded him and disgracefully spat on his face, accusing him of conspiracy with the monkeys who had come and destroyed their melons. They threatened that they would punish him for his mischievous activities. He denied this charge absolutely but asked the girls if there was anything they would like him to do for them. They had tried for a long time to get some perfume-like herbs which an old man grew not very far from there, but the old man was ever so watchful and they were unable to get them. They asked Mwathi if he could help them to get some. He assured them that he would do them this favour and asked them to come with him to the old man's field the following afternoon. Mwathi knew that the old man was very fond of snuff. He bought some so that he could make a present to the old man.

The following afternoon, Mwathi met the girls and he told them that, when he had engaged the old man in a conversation and made him lie down on his back, so that he could give him a pedicure and remove jiggers from his feet, they should collect as many herbs as they wanted, and as soon as they had collected enough, they should run away laughing merrily; then he would know that all was well. The girls promised to comply with Mwathi's clever plan.

Mwathi went to the old man and gave him some snuff, pretending to be very kind. The old man was very grateful to Mwathi. They started chatting in a very friendly way when Mwathi offered to help the old man by removing jiggers from his feet and giving him a pedicure. The old man was only too glad to have this done as he was so much troubled by jiggers. He lay down readily and offered his feet to Mwathi.

The sun was shining, and together with the soothing movement of Mwathi's fingers on the old man's feet, the old man almost slept. Mwathi removed the jiggers very delicately and the old man felt happy and comforted after having been troubled by these parasites for so long.

By the time Mwathi finished this operation, the girls had gathered all the beautiful flowers and herbs from the old man's field. As arranged, they laughed merrily as they left the field. The old man was surprised to hear their voices and at once suspected that something sinister was going on. He sat up quickly and told Mwathi that the girls might have come to steal his herbs. He looked towards the direction from where he heard the voices of the girls, and to his surprise he saw them walking away carrying loads of herbs which they had stolen from his field. He was very angry. He shouted and asked them to return his herbs. He cursed them, but they went away laughing merrily. The old man's feet were aching and he could not run after them.

Mwathi expressed his profound sympathy with the old man, and apologized profusely that his kindness should have been followed by such an unhappy event; he then offered to do anything to help the old man. The old man told Mwathi that he was grateful for what he had already done but wondered if Mwathi had some more snuff left. Mwathi was only too happy to give the old man all the snuff he had with him. The snuff was of a special quality and the old man was contented.

That was the end of Mwathi's debts, and he resolved never again to get so much involved in such tragic affairs. He returned to his sweet-potato field and cultivated his land and lived happily ever after.

The
Twilight Song of Honey-bird

IN THE late afternoon when the sun goes down on the western
horizon with its brilliant and beautiful golden yellow colour,
Gikuyu herd boys with their cattle, goats, and flocks of sheep
would carefully check if their animals were all in the group,
and would call them by their names: 'Nyange, Njiru, Thiru'
and so on, and the animals would answer by mooing and
bleating.

The fields, down the valleys or up on the hills or on the
plains, would be drowned in the loud echoes of the singing and
whistling of the boys and of the mooing and bleating of the
cows and goats and sheep, longing to return home to suckle
their young. The boys would sing back and forth to one another
as they came down the hills and their voices would travel across
the valleys.

The herd boys had one common and familiar song which
they sang to one another in turn. It was the 'Twilight Song of
Honey-bird', which was sung in praise and appreciation of a
bird that collected and ate honey as bees do, flying from flower
to flower. It was a beautiful bird, small in size, with yellow-
golden, green, and pinkish feathers which matched the colour
of the setting tropical sun. The bird had a long yellow beak
with which she busily collected the honey from the flowers
before she retired to her nest as the sun faded away and darkness descended. Her songs as she ate the honey enchanted the
herd boys who composed the song in her honour:

Kanyua njui, kanyua njui	Honey-bird, Honey-bird
Ndurute migui, ndurute migui	Get arrows, get arrows;
Ruta migui, ruta migui	Get your arrows, get your arrows
Tukarathane, tukarathane;	We'll fight a duel, we'll fight a duel;
Na wandatha, na wandatha	Then if you beat me, if you beat me
Ngaguthinjira, ngaguthinjira;	I'll slaughter you a lamb, I'll slaughter you a lamb;
Nacio nyama, nacio nyama	Then the meat, the meat
Ukahee aturi, ukahee aturi;	Will be given to the smiths, will be given to the smiths;
Nao aturi, nao aturi	Then the smiths, the smiths
Mature tuhiu, mature tuhiu;	Will make knives, the smiths will make knives;
Natuo tuhiu, natuo tuhiu	Then the knives, the knives
Tuheo ethaga, tuheo ethaga;	Will be given to the rainmakers, will be given to the rainmakers;
Nao ethaga, nao ethaga	Then the rainmakers, the rainmakers
Makoiria mbura, makoiria mbura;	Will make rain, will make rain;
Nayo mbura, nayo mbura	Then the rain, the rain
Tgakuria nyeki, igakuria nyeki	Will grow grass, will grow grass;
Nayo nyeki, nayo nyeki	Then the grass, the grass
Ikarera njau, ikarera njau;	Will feed the calves, will feed the calves;

57

Nacio njau, nacio njau	Then the calves, the calves
Ikagura muka, ikagura muka;	Will buy a wife, will buy a wife;
Nake muka, nake muka	Then the wife, the wife
Agakia ukie, agakia ukie;	Will grind a paste, will grind a paste;
Naguo ukie, naguo ukie	Then the paste, the paste
Akaruga mote, akaruga mote;	She'll cook porridge, she'll cook porridge;
Nayo mote, nayo mote	Then the porridge, the porridge
Tukahondoria,	
tukahondoria—	We'll eat, we'll eat—
S-s-s-s-s-s-r-o-o-o-o-ro-o!	S-s-s-s-s-s-r-o-o-o-o-ro-o!

The Man and the Dove

Once upon a time a man was travelling home from a long safari. He had to cross a sandy, dry and rugged region which separated his home country-side and Yata, where he had gone to do some business. This area was full of most dangerous animals and snakes.

Just a day before his journey was over, he had exhausted his food and his water which he had carried with him. It was very hot. At sunset he came to a rocky escarpment which separated the arid region from the higher fertile and vegetated country-side where he lived. It was a great relief to see trees and grass again. He was longing for a shady place to sit and have a little rest.

At the base of the escarpment there was a big tree which stood against a great mass of rock. He went and sat under the shade, and looking around he saw drops of what he thought was water dripping down rapidly from somewhere above the tree. Moved by his great thirst and without bothering to find out whether it was drinkable water, he pulled out his drinking vessel and held it under the drops, to fill it. When there was just enough to drink, a dove suddenly came from somewhere above and knocked down the vessel before he could drink. The water poured out on to the ground. He was very angry, but before he could hit the bird it had disappeared into the great tree.

The man picked his vessel up and went back to get some more water, and just before he could drink the dove knocked the vessel again so that it fell on the ground. This happened

about three times, but instead of trying to find out why this bird was so daring in interfering with his drink, he decided to kill it. So when he tried to draw his water for the fourth time he carefully calculated the movement of the bird, and just before it could hit the vessel he struck it first.

The dove lay helplessly on the ground, dying slowly, with both wings broken. The man was happy now that he was going to drink his water without any interference. He looked at the dove, feeling triumphant, and to his surprise he noticed that the bird was making a last effort to convey a message to him. At once he felt that there was something the bird was trying to tell him. The dove cried in a very sad voice which sounded almost human and at this instant it looked above towards the direction of the dropping water as though to tell the man to look up. He turned his head and to his horror he saw an enormous poisonous snake. It was lying amongst the rocks above and resting its head in the tree. The water was coming from its mouth, intended to poison the man purposely so that it could catch him and swallow him up. It had killed many people this way and the bird had witnessed many incidents of this nature and was determined to pass the message to human beings so that they could kill the snake and save themselves as well as other harmless creatures of nature also victimized by its great evil.

The man felt ashamed of himself for his cruelty to the bird. He tried to help the bird but it was too late. It died, but satisfied it had succeeded in passing the message. The man took up his things and ran home as fast as his feet could carry him. He summoned all the warriors in his neighbourhood and informed them of the dangerous snake on the tree and confirmed that all their missing neighbouring merchants, who had travelled along the same route as he had done, had indeed been poisoned and devoured by a snake, as rumours and suspicions had had it for so long.

The following morning, therefore, they carried a carcass of goat with a deadly African poison in it, and placed it under the tree. They surrounded the place and, hiding in the thickets, they waited for the snake to descend for its meal. Thinking that the warriors had gone, it came down and quickly swallowed the carcass. Usually the poison in the goat does not take effect until it has been digested. As the snake was tired and helplessly gorged with the goat carcass, the men were able to attack it and kill it without much resistance. They slashed it into pieces with their swords and they made a big fire and burnt it into ashes, to make sure that it was destroyed for ever.

The Girl and the Drought

ONCE upon a time there was a very pretty girl who was greatly loved by her parents. She was very hard-working, obedient, and chaste. Her father refused her permission to marry many young men who proposed to her. He wanted her to marry a man of good character and from a good family.

One day the girl met a boy who was approved of by her father, and the boy's father also approved of the relationship. Arrangements were made for the payment of marriage dowries and for the customary celebrations and festivities which precede the wedding ceremony. The girl and her lover, their relations and friends were very happy and looked forward to these occasions which were regarded as very important in Gikuyu social life.

At this time a great drought came and the whole country was threatened with famine. The witch-doctors, seers, and prophets investigated the cause of the drought. The rain-makers of Gikuyu assembled frequently and tried to make rain by their magic. The wise old holy men, who made rain sacrifice to the Gikuyu God, said their prayers, but all in vain. As the days passed by, numerous sacrifices were offered to God, but without any success, and the tribe was getting weary, and feared that they might have committed an unforgivable sin.

When all sorts of possible causes for the lack of rain had been exhausted, the wise men, prophets, and witch-doctors started wondering whether God wanted a human sacrifice instead of the goats and lambs as the Gikuyu custom required. They went to probe this question, and said their prayers under the sacred trees and on top of Mount Kenya. They wanted God to direct them what to do to get rain. One witch-doctor came out with an answer. He said that there was one girl in the tribe whom God wanted sacrificed. She would be taken to Thagana River and would get into the river by herself, and as soon as she was submerged, rain would fall and the tribe would prosper again. The witch-doctor indicated that the girl was the one who was about to be wedded.

This news was a great tragedy to the girl and her family, and also to the boy who was going to marry her. The boy wanted to defy the findings of the witch-doctors, but his father warned him not to be foolish, saying that the girl was unclean and would bring misfortune to his house as she had done to the tribe. The boy accepted his father's advice, though reluctantly, for he was much in love with the girl.

The girl's father was most grieved. He wanted to give his own life to let his daughter live. He consulted many witch-doctors and wise men in the hope that the findings of the other witch-doctors were false. His efforts were in vain. It was confirmed by many wise men, seers, and witch-doctors of the tribe that the girl was unclean, and had to be sacrificed as ordained by the God of Gikuyu.

When the girl learned that nothing could be done to make God accept a different kind of sacrifice, she resolved not to resist His wish. She loved her tribe more than her sweetheart and would feel even more satisfied if she saved her tribe from famine. She consented to offer herself as a sacrifice to please God and bring prosperity to her people.

On the day appointed by the witch-doctors for the sacrifice, the girl walked to the bank of the river. Dressed in her bridal dress, she looked very beautiful. She showed no sign of fear or strain, but looked most cheerful, and smiled to the people who came to watch the ordeal. The parents and relations of the girl were sad, and her friends were crying; but she, surprisingly, was looking happier and gayer than ever before. She sang as she went down to the river:

Wamunyori witu,	My beloved one,
Wanjugu,	My sweetheart,
Niwareka ngora?	You let me perish;
Ngora na mugambo,	I am cursed and doomed to
Wanjugu, na mbura ndikoira;	perish,
Mbura ura!	My sweetheart, the rain
Kirindi kiiganire!	wouldn't fall;
	May rain now come;
	May the tribe now prosper!

She walked down to the river singing most beautifully. She could be heard from every corner of the country, yet to those who were near the river and actually saw her, the voice seemed normal, and they could not guess that it could be heard from anywhere beyond. As she came to the bank of the river, a cloud started forming in the sky. She walked slowly into the water, pausing at each step, and sang her song to her lover and to her friends. Her face was shining like the light of the morning sun, and her teeth were shining like pearls when she smiled and sang. Now people who saw her did believe that she was the cause of the drought, and that she must have been sent from God. Nothing of the sort had ever been seen in the country.

She continued to descend into the water, slowly, singing. As she went down, darkness caused by the clouds in the sky began to fall on the country, and people began to be afraid, even the wise men, seers, witch-doctors, and rain-makers. When the girl's head was completely submerged and she disappeared into the river, a heavy storm began. There was lightning and thunder, and in a very short time, rain fell throughout the Gikuyu country, and the tribe was saved from famine. From then on the Gikuyu country became blessed by God with numerous rivers and plenty of rain through the seasons, and the people became wealthy and happy, and God instructed the seers, wise men, witch-doctors, and rain-makers to make regular sacrifices of lambs. That was the first human sacrifice and the last, and the tribe lived happily ever after.

The Girl and her Father's Gourd

ONCE upon a time there was a girl who feared her father very much. He was a very domineering man who punished his children severely for very trivial mistakes. He stopped them from touching his things, and always nagged his wife about the children's behaviour. He even beat his wife and the children whenever he was angry. He was really very cruel and brutal. The children of his neighbours feared him too. He was disliked by many people and children particularly hated him. Whenever they saw him passing, they ran away in terror.

His younger daughter was sent to draw water from the river and the mother was left at home, cooking. The girl while looking for her water calabash picked up her father's porridge calabash by mistake. Without looking carefully she just put it in the calabash basket and ran down the hill to the river. She pulled the calabash out of the basket and dipped it into the water to fill. As the water was flowing into the calabash she realized that she had taken her father's calabash which was not supposed to be filled with water as this would greatly spoil the taste of porridge. Her father was not going to like it! She was so worried that in her fright she lost her grip of the calabash, and it was washed away by the stream.

'Oh, dear!' she cried, 'my father's calabash! Please stop, come back, calabash!' She ran down the stream chasing after it and crying loudly,

'Please come back, calabash, my father's calabash! Come back! I shall be beaten tonight! Please don't let him beat me, please come back, calabash!'

She ran through the fields and bushes, beside the stream, hoping to recover the calabash. Whenever she saw somebody by the water she asked,

'Have you seen my father's calabash go by?'

'Yes,' they replied, 'but that was hours ago and the calabash must be miles away by now. You had better return home, you silly girl.'

This did not deter her, but she went on running beside the stream, hoping to recover her father's calabash.

Just before sunset, she came to a low region where the river was almost still, and there she saw her father's calabash floating, held at the bank of the river by the growth. She picked it up, but when she looked across the river she saw, to her horror, many crocodiles swimming fast towards her. She quickly ran away from the river, when an old man saw her and asked her,

'Who are you, my child, and what are you doing at this very dangerous part of the river?'

'I came to fetch my father's calabash which was washed down by the river,' she replied. She explained to the old man how she had picked up the wrong calabash, and how she was afraid of her father who was a very cruel man.

The old man was very understanding and sympathetic. He decided to take the girl back to her home and speak to her father. He explained to the girl's father how she had risked her life chasing the gourd down the stream to the crocodile-infested region and how she escaped being caught by them while picking up the calabash. When her father heard this he swore never again to be cruel to children, and from then on-wards, his children loved him dearly, and they lived happily ever after.

The Monster that Never Was

Once upon a time there lived a widow who had a pretty daughter. The mother wanted the companionship of her daughter and for a long time she discouraged many suitors who wished to marry the girl. She was very possessive and selfish and disregarded her daughter's feelings. They had a farm on which they grew millet, corn, beans, and vegetables.

One season they found that their young and delicate crop was being eaten by some mysterious animal. Each time they put in new plants they were cut down and destroyed while still young. The poor woman and her daughter were worried because they did not know what sort of animal was attacking their crop.

One day the woman decided to build a hut in the field and make a fire at night to scare the animal which was destroying the crop. While she sat by the fire in the evening she saw a glow of light coming towards her and at the same time she heard a very deep voice singing:

> *Ndiranagia! Ndiranagia!*
> *Matunguru, mwenyenyo!*
> *Ndiranagia!*

which means:

> I cut, I cut the young crop,
> I shake them
> I fell them
> I cut, I cut the young crop.

68

The voice was so loud that at first the woman thought it was thunder and that the glow was lightning. But as the singing continued and the light drew nearer and nearer she realized that this was the creature which was destroying her crop.

She was so terrified that she ran for her life. When she got home she fainted and remained unconscious for hours.

After she had recovered from the shock she told her daughter about this terrible monster, the like of which she had never seen before. Then she offered to pay a lot of money to any man who could kill the 'lightning animal', as she called it.

Many men tried to scare the animal at night, but all of them were so terrified by its thunderous voice that they ran for their lives. The woman was getting anxious as the rainy season was passing and she was afraid that they would starve during the dry season as there would be no food for them. She began to offer even larger sums of money, but nobody would take it. So at last she asked her daughter if she would marry any man who succeeded in killing the animal, and her daughter agreed.

Now there was a poor boy in the village who had always admired the widow's daughter, but because he was so poor she would not have anything to do with him. When the boy heard of this offer he went straight to the woman and her daughter and said that he would kill the animal, provided he would be allowed to marry the pretty girl. The girl did not raise any objection and so the boy went to the field that night with his weapons, ready to kill the animal or to be killed himself.

While he sat by the fire waiting for the monster to come he suddenly saw the glow of light over by the other side of the farm and a thunderous voice began to chant the dreadful tune which was by this time feared by the whole village. For a moment the boy thought of running for his life, but thinking of his lowly position he knew that nobody would miss him if he died. However if he killed the monster he would marry the girl he always loved and be able to build up a family of his own. At this thought he decided to die rather than run home in a cowardly fashion.

The animal was still singing and coming nearer and nearer and the boy was trembling with fear while he waited. When the light was close to him and the voice quite distinct, he looked with fear and horror, and to his great surprise, instead of seeing a big monster he saw a tiny creature with a glow of light at its tail. It was a glow-worm. He caught it and wrapped it up in a piece of rag which he tore from his shirt. After that there was no more lightning nor the thunderous voice singing the terrible song that had made so many men quake with fear and horror.

The boy walked home the following morning proudly and with confidence. He was going to be wedded to the girl he had always loved and whom many a man had miserably failed to win. As he arrived home he told the woman that he had caught the animal alive and asked her to summon the village to witness his victory and to bless him and his bride.

When the woman had called the villagers, the boy produced the tiny glow-worm from his pocket. They all burst into laughter and ridiculed him, but without feeling embarrassed he asked them to listen. Then he gently touched the tail of the worm and suddenly it started sparkling with a powerful and blinding light and produced the famous but dreaded music which so many people had heard and feared. Then they all agreed that this was the animal that they wanted to see killed. The glow-worm was destroyed there and then, and the boy was wedded to the pretty girl whom he had always loved and wanted to marry, and they lived happily ever after.

The Poor Man of Iruri

ONCE upon a time there was a very poor man who lived with his three sons at Iruri, a green common with many pools of salty water. Many herdsmen from the neighbouring villages grazed their sheep and cattle there. Farmers from distant places also brought their animals to Iruri to graze and drink the salty water. The poor man of Iruri did not have any sheep, goats, or cattle, and his sons used to worry him with many questions:

'Father, we would like to be good herdsmen. Where are our animals?' they would ask.

'Don't you worry, my sons, you are rich and noble. The only thing I want you to learn quickly and perfectly is how to be good soldiers,' he would answer his sons.

The old man did not want to tell his sons that he was poor. This would depress them, and might cause them to run away from home and take to vagrancy. He knew that if they became good soldiers, they would capture sheep, goats, and cattle in tribal wars.

The three boys used to wander all over the green common. They went about shooting birds with their toy arrows, and hunting rabbits with their small spears. They played with other boys, children of the herdsmen who came to graze their animals on the common. They learned to be good herdsmen by joining their friends who came with their fathers to the common every day. But as they grew up they began to realize that they should know more about their own property, and they continued to ask their father about their position.

'Father, whose land is this common?' they would ask.

'I have told you, my sons, you are rich and noble. I want you to learn how to use your spears, swords, bows, and arrows, and when you are good soldiers, I shall then tell you all you want to know about my property, and what I shall leave you when I die.'

The three boys grew up and became very strong men. They learned the tribal warrior techniques, and became great tribal warriors who were feared throughout the country. Their father was growing old and weak, and his days were coming to an end. He was pleased with his sons. He was confident that they were going to carry out his advice on how to be successful, when he was gone.

One day the poor man fell ill. He knew he was going to die. He called his sons to his bedside one evening to give them his last instructions.

'My beloved sons,' he said, 'I am going to my eternal place of rest. I have always promised to tell you about my property. Listen to me very carefully. This whole fertile land you see is mine, and all the sheep, goats, and cattle that graze here daily are mine. The herdsmen you see here daily are my servants. I am leaving now and I give you all my property, and ask you to supervise the whole estate, giving your orders to my servants as you please. I advise you to become good soldiers because I know that this world is full of evil men, and you might be denied your own rights when I am gone, and unless you are able to fight, you might be condemned to poverty.'

He finished speaking. 'But father, father,' they said, 'why did you not let us know this before?'

'I have told you now,' he replied, 'you are men now, and you can fight, fight, fight, fight . . .' and he continued to repeat the word 'fight' in an emphatic, but fading voice, and he did not say anything more. Then he died.

The three brothers were filled with sorrow at their father's death and fear at the news he had broken to them of their ownership of the property, some of which was in the hands of very strong families they knew very well. They gave their father a solemn burial the following day. Although they informed their neighbours, no one came to the funeral, and none of them observed the customary days of mourning. This infuriated the three young men who regarded these neighbours as their servants, as their father had told them.

When mourning was over, they decided to expel most of their servants and take up herding themselves. One day when the herdsmen came to the common, the three brothers came to them and asked them to leave the job and the animals. The herdsmen were puzzled, and thought perhaps the three brothers had gone mad because of their father's death. They ignored the orders given by the young men, and at once trouble started. The three brothers armed with their spears, arrows, and swords, fought the herdsmen, killing many on the spot. Some of them ran for their lives, leaving their cattle, sheep, and goats. The three brothers took all the animals on the common, and became the richest men of the Gikuyu country. But whenever there are property disputes among the Gikuyu, the elders always tease one another,

'Don't ape the poor man of Iruri.'

The Story of Moon and Sun

Once upon a time the kingdom of the sky was ruled by one great king. Moon and Sun were the only children he had. He married many wives, hoping to increase the number of his children, but they all failed to give him any children.

So he divorced all of them except the mother of Moon and Sun. She was a very good mother to her sons and a good wife to her husband. But nature was most unkind, for she died when Sun was very young.

The king of the sky looked after his sons and was particularly very fond of Sun, his younger son. Moon was possessive and very jealous of his brother. He always treated Sun unkindly.

When their father was about to die, he called Moon and Sun to his bedside to receive his last blessings. He divided his kingdom into two dukedoms to be governed by his two sons, and he divided his wealth between them.

As Sun was still very young, in fact too young to take such responsibility as ruling a half of the sky kingdom, Moon was requested by his father to act as Sun's regent until Sun became of age to rule his dukedom.

Also Moon was requested to be trustee of half of the wealth that had to go to Sun, and to find a good wife for Sun when he wanted to marry. According to custom, Moon would have to pay the bride price or dowry on behalf of Sun.

Moon promised his father to be kind to Sun and to hand over his dukedom and property when Sun became of age. The king of the sky blessed his sons, and then he died.

After the death of their father, Moon became unmindful of

his brother Sun. He treated him like a servant or a beggar. Whenever Sun wanted something Moon always denied it to him. Moon's wife was also very unkind to Sun.

Moon wanted to retain the sky kingdom in one unit and make himself the sole ruler.

When Sun wished to marry he went to ask his brother for cattle, goats, and sheep in order to make an offer to his future father-in-law, but Moon would not give him any.

When Sun became of age and demanded permission to rule his dukedom Moon refused completely and denied that their father had intended to divide the kingdom. He said that he was the elder son and as such he was the right and only heir. Moon threatened to kill his brother when Sun complained about this injustice.

So Sun had to run away for his safety. He went away and decided never to return. He went a long way away from his country into a foreign country with which his father had had good relations. He did not, however, reveal his identity for fear that his brother might follow him and endanger his life.

Sun went to the homestead of the king of this foreign country. The king had many wives, and many children, but they were all girls.

Sun asked the king to employ him as a shepherd. He was employed, and he lived within the king's homestead. He worked hard and earned the admiration of everyone in the homestead. He was regarded as one of the family.

Sun fell in love with one of the daughters of the homestead. The girl was the favourite child of the king and the king had decided that this daughter would be the heir of his kingdom and so should not be allowed to marry anyone who would take her out of the family. Her husband was to be from one of the noble families within the kingdom.

This made things difficult for Sun, who was regarded as a poor herdsman and whose family was not known by the king. Sun was tempted to reveal his identity but feared the embarrassment.

He also feared that if his brother Moon was consulted, his

position might be worse. Perhaps Moon would deny Sun's identity or order his deportation. Sun decided to remain as he was and try to win the king over, as he had done as a shepherd.

Near the king's homestead there was a large, beautiful lake.

In the middle of the lake there was an island of beautiful feathers. They looked like ostrich feathers. Their colours were as the colours of the rainbow. People used to travel from distant places to come to see these magic feathers in the middle of the lake.

Nobody had ever been anywhere near them. Many great sailors had attempted to row their boats near the feathers and they had all mysteriously perished before reaching them.

The king had consulted many witch-doctors to tell him what sort of animal it was that lived in the middle of the lake.

This mystery was associated with his family, by many witch-doctors and seers. Some said that the existence of these feathers brought ill spirits to the king's family and that was why he was unable to have any sons by his wives.

The king had offered much money to many good sailors to go to the middle of the lake and bring back some of the feathers. Many had perished in the attempt.

To stop many young men from disturbing his daughter, the king made a condition that the only man who would be allowed to marry his beloved girl, would be the man who succeeded in reaching the beautiful feathers, in the middle of the lake, and bringing some of them to him.

All this time Sun was doing well with his work as a herdsman. The king's daughter continued to like him. She thought that one day she would be able to persuade her father to accept Sun as her husband and also to persuade Sun to agree to live within and perpetuate the king's family.

One day Sun decided to go to the lake and find out what animal bore the beautiful magical feathers that floated on the surface of the lake. He realized that it must be a great sea monster. Instead of sailing, or rowing a boat, he decided to swim under the water and take the animal by surprise.

The king's daughter refused to agree to Sun's plan, because

she loved him dearly and did not want him to be devoured by the great monster. But Sun persisted and said that he knew how to kill the animal and that he was going to succeed.

He told her that he was deeply in love with her and could not wait any more. He would rather die in his attempt to kill the monster than live in such misery. He was sure he was going to be safe and would return to marry her at once.

Sun and the king's daughter went to her mother to tell her of their love. She in turn told the king, who was dismayed at this news. But as he knew that the sea monster was unconquerable he gave his word that if Sun would bring the feathers from the middle of the lake 'he would be allowed to marry his favourite daughter.

Sun was very pleased. He prepared a long strong rope made of leather wound round a hollow tube. The rope was miles long. He asked the king to give him the best sword and spear in the homestead. Sun went to a good witch-doctor to get magic medicine with which to stupefy the sea monster, and also some poison to kill it with. He poisoned his sword and spear, and when he was ready, Sun asked the daughter of the king to promise that she would stay on the shore and hold the rope while he swam towards the monster. She promised to do this.

Now that all the preparations were ready, Sun asked the king to summon his neighbours to come to the shore of the lake and witness his venture. It was a fine morning. The people were gathered by the lake. Sun knotted the rope about his waist and put one end of it in his mouth, leaving the other end on the shore to be held by his beloved. This served as a breathing apparatus.

He dived into the water with his spear and sword.

He swam for days and nights, and the girl stayed by the shore of the lake uncoiling the rope as Sun swam towards the monster. She prayed God that Sun might be victorious. Of all the men who had proposed to her she was convinced that Sun was the only one who was really and genuinely in love with her.

Even the king himself was beginning to respect Sun. He regretted having insisted on Sun's fetching the feathers. He ordered his daughter to try and call Sun back. He said he was sure Sun was a good man and she would have his permission to marry him.

It was not easy to get Sun back. To pull the rope might endanger Sun's life. There was no means of communication, to convey the news to Sun that he now had the approval of the king and that his present labour was no longer necessary.

So Sun swam on.

One day at about noon, the people on the shore of the lake saw the blue water in the middle of the lake turn red. It became a pool of blood.

They were seized with great fear. Sun must have been killed, they thought for a moment.

The king's daughter fainted, and her mother came to hold the rope, and shook it to find if it were loose the other end.

But she could feel some object still clinging to the rope. She kept on holding it, while other people were attending to her daughter who was crying for her lover.

All at once the people could see a peculiar movement in the feathers. They thought that the animal was coming to kill them after killing Sun.

When the girl regained consciousness, she was told that the feathers were moving towards the shore, and she held the rope again; she could feel something at the other end. Placing her ear against the end of the rope, she could hear Sun's breath and was sure that Sun was safe.

Sun had killed the great monster.

He reached it from behind when it was asleep, with its head above the water. When the sun was shining, the monster usually kept its head above the water. Also, to protect its precious, beautiful feathers, the monster had to keep its head above water most of the time during the day, so that it could watch out for any intruders.

When Sun got near the monster he approached its neck, without its seeing him, and with his poisoned spear he killed it at one stroke, by sending the spear straight through its heart.

Then he cut its throat with several rapid strokes of the sword.

The monster died almost instantly, without much struggle. And Sun chopped off the tail with its beautiful feathers and carried it with him towards the shore.

He swam back for days and nights, and when the weather was clear he waved to the people ashore. They realized then he had killed the monster. Many people came from far and near.

They wanted to witness Sun's victory and to attend the wedding of the daughter of the king.

Eventually help was sent to Sun to bring him back but he would not get on a boat. He wanted to finish his work the way he planned to do it.

When he stepped ashore he was embraced by his beloved. Yet before they had a moment to say anything, the people were amazed by the sight of cows emerging from the lake. The cows came out in great numbers. They came out in so great a number that people who were counting them could not count them any more. Their eyes were tired.

Then out came the bulls, as many as the cows.

Then came the calves, as many as the cows.

Then came goats, as many as the cows and bulls. Then out came sheep, as many as the cows, bulls, calves, and goats. The whole place was now drowned with the noise of these herds of cattle, goats, and sheep. They were so many that no kingdom had such large herds.

The king was very happy and proud of Sun. He had conquered the great monster that had killed so many people. The herds of cattle, goats, and sheep were those the monster had stolen from the kingdom over the years, and had magically lived in its stomach.

The feathers of the great monster were used to thatch the king's houses within the homestead. Some were spared to thatch the new home of the bride and the bridegroom.

At this stage Sun revealed his identity and expressed his desire to return to his country and claim his dukedom from his brother Moon. The king was overjoyed to learn this, as the father of Sun had been a great friend of the king, before he died.

Preparations were made to wed Sun to the king's daughter and to escort them to Sun's home.

When Sun reached his home with his bride, the beautiful feathers, and a large herd of cattle, goats, and sheep, his brother was very surprised. He, in fact, felt very jealous, for Sun now was many times richer than Moon. Sun's wife was prettier than Moon's wife.

But Sun was very kind and gentle. He forgave his brother and gave him some of the feathers to thatch his house with.

Moon could not be reconciled with his brother. Although he accepted the gifts given to him by Sun, he was still jealous and thought of doing his brother more harm.

One day, while they were grazing their animals, Moon planned to kill Sun. He asked Sun to go down a salty clay mine and dig some salty clay for their animals.

While Sun was in the mine Moon buried him alive and returned home alone with the animals.

He informed Sun's wife that her husband had had an accident at the mines and was buried there.

She was very sad. She went to the mine to try and dig her husband out, but it was too late. He was dead. She went back to her father with this sad news. Her mother comforted her and promised that she was going to do something about it.

The mother went to a famous witch-doctor who was reputed for reviving the dead. She learnt all the magic of reviving the dead and came back to her daughter.

She instructed her to go to the mine and cut bits of flesh from every part of Sun's body and put them in a clean calabash and take them back home to her house.

When she got home she was to hide the calabash somewhere in the house and she was to put some fat and minced meat into the calabash regularly until all the bits of flesh in the calabash were composed into a small body, by magic. Then Sun's wife would break the calabash and hide the small body somewhere else in her house and continue to feed it with delicate foods particularly milk and meat.

She had to be nice to Moon so that he would give her as

much meat as she would ask of him. Moon, who by custom, regarded himself as the husband of Sun's wife was only too willing to give her anything, at any time.

She fed the small body with the delicacies, as she was advised by her mother, and gradually Sun's body was magically transformed from his dead body away off in the mines into the new body in his house.

The process was gradual but quick, and Sun's wife kept up her demand for meat and delicate food.

By the time the mourning days for Sun's death were over, Sun was complete and back in his house in exactly the same form and shape as before.

According to the custom, Moon would have to go to the house of Sun's wife at the end of the mourning and stay in the house with her as his bride.

For this occasion Moon had organized a big feast and had invited many people from near and far, including Mrs Sun's family, to come to witness Moon's new wedding.

Of course, Sun and his wife and her family knew what had happened and what was going to happen on the day proposed for the re-wedding of Sun's wife to Moon.

It was arranged by plan that Sun would emerge again on that day, and that he would expose Moon in the presence of all the people. Then they would try Moon and a decision would be reached so that Moon should cease troubling his brother in future.

Sun was sent the most magnificent robes, spear, sword and an elder's staff for the occasion.

On the appointed day people from the whole country came to the feast. Moon had made a lot of beer. There were all sorts of things to eat—meat from the biggest bulls, goats, and sheep. Moon had also had a lot of gifts from his subjects, beer, honey and bananas, and all sorts of delicacies were brought from distant places as gifts.

Moon was filled with joy that he was going to have a new young and pretty wife; now he was going to rank as the richest man in the sky.

When the people were congregated in the royal homestead and all the guests were waiting for the ceremony, the father of Sun's wife stood up and called for the attention of the people.

The place at once became silent. One could even hear the noise of a fly flapping its small wings. This was the first time a ruler of a foreign country had stood before them to speak. The king said that before making any speech, he would ask his daughter to come out of the house first. At this point he called her by name and asked her to come out.

To everybody's surprise she came out followed by Sun holding her hand. This was like a dream to many people who had been led to believe that Sun was dead, and a great horror to Moon who was so guilty of his crimes: expelling his brother from home, depriving him of his heritage, and killing him when he returned.

Moon collapsed from shock and it was hours before he recovered.

While he was recovering from the shock people were shouting, asking Sun to kill Moon with his spear.

'Kill him! kill him, Sun!' they cried, 'he is an evil man, kill him!'

'Calm, please calm,' he pleaded, 'I do not believe in revenge. I shall ask you first to listen to what I have to say and then I shall expect you to make your own judgement.'

'Let us hear,' they shouted. 'What happened?'

Sun told the whole story, from their father's death, and the will, his banishment, and how he was murdered and magically revived by his wife.

The people were satisfied that Moon was an evil man and all agreed that he should be banished far away into the sky and that he should live by night while Sun ruled and lived by day.

That is why the moon is seen at night and sun during the day.

The Boy and Nyange the Cow

ONCE upon a time there was a boy who looked after his father's herd very carefully and was most obedient and devoted to his father. He was a very good and skilled herdsman; his animals knew him well and liked him. His father was a very cruel, fierce, and brutal man and was feared by his children.

The boy spent the whole of his time looking after the cattle and when he went home in the evenings he was given a lot of work by his father. He did not visit his friends and did not attend the tribal dances which were held in the villages for other boys and girls of his age group. He grew without any kind of social life, and was very unhappy all the time.

While he grazed the cattle in the fields he would sing to himself, and always sang very sad songs. He was very lonely, and everyone pitied him. He was a handsome boy, admired by many girls, but he did not have a chance even to speak to them. Nyange, one of the cows in his herd, was the only friend he could count on. He liked Nyange very much and used to give her nice fodder to eat, and when he went to salty clay mines he always carried home the nicest parts of the salty clay for Nyange. He also gave her other delicacies liked by cattle. Nyange loved him very much. When he was not near her she would moo and moo until he appeared. She seemed to understand the boy's unhappy position and always kept him company by grazing close to him while they were in the fields. The boy would speak to her as though she were human. He did not expect her to understand him, but surprisingly, Nyange understood everything the boy said; whenever he ordered her to go away, or to come to him, or to eat something, she always did as he told her. Though this made the boy curious it caused him to like Nyange even more. Nyange could not speak, but she understood human language!

Besides ordering Nyange to come here, or go there, or eat this or that as the boy had been doing, he started asking her to stop one cow or even a bull in the herd from going far away from the other animals, and each time Nyange would go and bring the straying animal back to the herd. This made the boy very happy and he liked Nyange more than ever. He had now a comrade who sympathized with him and gave him help. He and Nyange became very great friends. In the mornings Nyange would moo, and moo in the shed until she saw him. While he let the cattle out of the shed he would scratch Nyange's ears and neck while she licked his hands. Nowhere had there been a cow like her.

When the boy grew up and became a strong young man he became more miserable than ever, for he did not have the chance to attend the traditional dances such as 'gicukia', 'kamano', 'mugoiyo', or 'kibata' which were seasonally conducted in the villages by the young men of his age group. He became most unhappy and hated his father who spent most of his time at beer parties and wandered all over the villages drinking beer. He was a bad father and an alcoholic who was despised as a bad example as an elder. Good fathers relieved their sons and gave them a chance to meet and play with their friends.

One day the boy thought of asking Nyange to look after the cattle while he attended a dance at a near-by village. Mysteriously Nyange understood and agreed to do him this favour. He went away and left the cattle in the field under Nyange's care. In the evening about sunset the boy returned and found the cattle properly under Nyange's control and was really grateful to her for being so helpful. He was glad that now he could attend dances while Nyange looked after the cattle. He became a regular dancer and made many friendships with boys and girls. He always returned to the field at sunset to fetch the cattle and took them home. Each day he stood at the top of the field and sang:

Nyange! Nyange!	Nyange! Nyange!
Thiururuka ciuke-i! Nyange;	Round them, bring them Nyange;
Kurigutuka-i! Nyange;	Night has come, Nyange,
Tuinuke mucii-i! Nyange!	Let's go home! Nyange!

Nyange went round the herd, and then walked in front of them and then they would follow her mooing, longing to return home and suckle their calves. The young man took his cattle home and did not let anyone know about his friendship with Nyange, or how she helped him look after the herd. He did this many times and started having a real and full social life. Not only did he go to the tribal dances regularly but also visited the many girl friends whom he had met at the dances and stayed with them for most of the day while Nyange looked after the cattle.

Nyange was a good substitute for the herdsman, but in the case of an unexpected raid by Masais, who frequently came to steal Gikuyu cattle, she was helpless. One day the herdsman left his cattle under Nyange's care as usual and went to dance at a distant village. Some Masai thieves who had spied him for some time came and drove the whole herd away. Nyange mooed and made a terrible noise all over the field, and so did the rest of the cattle. The echo of their cry could be heard from afar, but it was useless; no one came to fight the Masai thieves. The cattle were driven over the Gikuyu-Masai border through the hills and forests into Masai cattle kraals.

When the young man returned and sang his song, there was no response, and going down into the field he found that there were no cattle. He remembered that Masai cattle thieves used to come to that neighbourhood, and could possibly have stolen his cattle. He was worried. He decided to follow the cattle. He followed the foot marks of the Masais and of the cattle. The trail went in the direction of Masai country. He was sure now the Masais had stolen his cattle. He was grieved, for fear of his father and because he would not have any cows to pay for a wife. He had already started proposing to one of the girls he had met at the dances. He was terrified and sad to lose his cattle. He kept on following the trail. He was not armed except that he had his simple spear and dagger and clubs which were generally carried by herdsmen to fight beasts if they attacked his herd. To fight a Masai thief he ought to have had a war spear, sword, and shield, and a stronger and thicker club. But he would not return home without the cattle or news of their whereabouts. So he went on resolved to find his cattle or die rather than return home without them.

He travelled a long way following the trail of his cattle through bushes and forests, up and down mountains, and across many rivers. Eventually he came to the Gikuyu-Masai border which he crossed without fear. He climbed a mountain and from the top he looked down and saw large herds of cattle being grazed in the valley below. As he had not lost the trail he realized that this place was where his cattle had been driven to. He spied carefully and there he could see Nyange among other cattle. This was the place where Masai thieves used to take stolen cattle before they eventually divided them among themselves. He feared to go down as he was alone and unarmed: the Masais would kill him. He stayed up there—worried and not knowing what to do.

The afternoon was sunny and beautiful. The brilliant rays of the setting sun lit the valley and its golden colours spread over the hill tops. The Masais were retiring to their fires, where they feasted on roast meat and drank milk. They sang songs of victories and praised E-Ngai who had given them so much cattle. They made many scornful references to their Gikuyu enemies who ate food polluted by their women and who did not know the art of cattle husbandry. The Masais sang that cattle was theirs by right and had to be taken from Agikuyu, who should stick to their natural work of tilling the land and leave cattle breeding to the Masais.

These songs horrified the young man. He thought over and

over again what he should do. Then he decided to sing his song to Nyange and see if she would bring the cattle to him. He whistled twice and sang his song to Nyange. He sang several times. Nyange heard him and so did the rest of his cattle. They mooed and became restless. Nyange with her tail raised in the air went round her herd, and all the cattle in her herd raised their tails in the air and went round the rest of other cattle which were also stolen from different parts of Gikuyu country, and Nyange ran in front of them while they followed her towards the mountain. The Masais did not hear the young man sing, nor did they see him, although they did gaze towards the top of the mountain.

What had become of the cattle? The Masais tried to run after them and stop the cattle from going towards the mountain. The cattle were furious and mad. They kicked and knocked some Masais down and trampled over them as they raced up the mountain. When the Masais saw how mad the cattle were they decided to let them go. They believed that the cattle were called by E-Ngai and that the rays of the sun which shone brightly over the mountain tops were eyes of E-Ngai, and they retired to their kraals to offer their prayers to E-Ngai and to seek forgiveness for their sins.

While the Masais were performing their religious rites, Nyange led the cattle up the mountain and the young man took them back on his own. It took him the whole night and half of the following day before he reached home. The Masai warriors had been stopped by their elders from following the cattle, as they agreed that the cattle were going to God and if the young Masais followed they would perish in the mountain. It was better to lose the cattle than warriors so the young Gikuyu herdsman was undisturbed throughout the journey home. He could stop at different places to graze and drink the animals, and he was even more confident about his safety when he crossed over into Gikuyu country. He led his cattle, which were now multiplied by hundreds, back home. He was whistling and singing proudly and confidently like a good herdsman.

All this time his father was angry and annoyed. He wandered

all over the villages and in the fields looking for his son and cattle. He had given them up. But he was surprised when he heard the cow bells, mooing and singing and the whistling of his son as he drove the herd back home. When they appeared from afar the people of the village came out to see these numerous cattle. They numbered many times more than what had ever been seen in the villages before. The women of the village yelled their welcome ... aari-rirririri-ri! five times as was the custom, and the father came forward to welcome his son. The young man reported what had happened and how Nyange had saved him and brought more cattle. The father was very happy and proud of his son and in gratitude he bought him a wife of his son's own choice, the girl he had met at the dances, and he and his wife lived happily ever after.

Wacici and her Friends

WACICI was a very beautiful girl, admired by many people for her elegance and charm. Her girl friends were very jealous of her and always ill-treated her.

One day her friends were going to visit a *mwehani** to have their teeth filed, spaced, and beautified as girls used to do. Wacici joined them. He was a man of great fame who was highly reputed for his skill. They all had their teeth well done and the girls looked very attractive and charming, but no one looked as pretty as Wacici. The expert praised Wacici's teeth and beauty and added that she had natural beauty and charm in everything. This annoyed her girl friends very much.

On their way home they stopped and talked to young men from time to time. They laughed as they spoke to the boys, 'Aha-aaa! Uuuuuu! Eia!' This is the most romantic laughter which was artificially employed by Gikuyu girls specially when speaking to boys. 'Aha-aaa! Uuuuuu! Eia! Aha-aaa! Uuuuuu! Eia!' They continued to laugh repeatedly as they spoke to young men and the boys would admire their teeth and their charm and sense of humour.

'You have been to the tooth expert, have you not?' the boys inquired.

'Aha-aaa! Uuuuuu! Eia!' The girls continued to laugh.

'Wacici is looking most attractive,' one boy remarked kindly, 'she is really gorgeous and wonderful.' And all the boys agreed and repeated this remark to Wacici. This infuriated the girls, who were very jealous of Wacici's beauty and many of them wanted her out of their company.

* An expert in beautifying teeth.

90

The girls continued their journey towards their homes and on the way they all conspired to bury Wacici alive in a porcupine hole which was somewhere in the forest near the road.

It was suggested that they should all enter the forest and gather some firewood to take back home as it was the custom that girls should return to their homes with some firewood after a day's outing. They all agreed to do this and Wacici particularly was very eager to take home some firewood. She was not only a beauty but also a very good girl who upheld the respect expected of Gikuyu girls, and her mother loved her dearly.

When the girls reached the porcupine hole in the forest, they grabbed Wacici and pushed her down the hole and quickly buried her alive. She was taken by surprise and she did not have a chance to scream as she thought that they were playing with her. They did not beat her or do anything harmful to her body. They sealed the hole very carefully on top, quickly left the forest and returned to their homes; they did not speak to anybody about Wacici.

That evening Wacici did not return home. Her parents waited and waited. When she did not come they went about asking Wacici's friends if they had been with her that day or whether they had seen her anywhere. They all denied having been with her or seeing her anywhere that day. All this time Wacici was crying in the bottom of the porcupine hole in the forest while her parents were wandering all over the villages looking for her.

'Where has she gone to?' her mother asked. 'Could a young man have eloped with her?' Her disappearance caused so much concern that her father had to go to consult witch-doctors and seers and ask what had become of his daughter.

Next morning Wacici's father met somebody who had seen his daughter in company of the other village girls going to the tooth expert. He reported this to his wife and without wasting any time he went to see the dentist in order to verify this information. The dentist confirmed that Wacici and her friends had been to see him and that he had done their teeth on the day she was reported missing. Also on his way home Wacici's father met some young men who had seen and spoken to his daughter with the other village girls. He returned home and reported to his wife and the family all the information he had gathered.

Wacici's brother, who knew most of the girls who were said to have been seen with his sister, had known for some time that most of the girls had been jealous, and hated Wacici. He suspected foul play.

He left home quickly and trekked the route through which the girls had returned from the expert. He knew that if they gathered some firewood, they must have entered the forest on the way. He went into the forest to check if his sister had been killed there.

When he came near the porcupine hole he noticed that it was freshly covered and that there were many footmarks which suggested that many people had been there. He examined them very carefully. He also saw a bundle of firewood which had been abandoned. This time Wacici could hear some noise and footsteps above her. She was crying and singing and calling her brother's name.

Cinji! Cinji!	Cinji! Cinji!
Nondakwirire-i! Cinji,	I already told you, Cinji,
Nothiganagwo-i! Cinji;	I have been hated and spied
Cinji! Cinji!	on, Cinji,
	Cinji! Cinji!

When he listened carefully he heard the voice of Wacici clearly and he had no doubt that she had been buried there by her girl friends who were jealous of her beauty. He called out, 'Wacici-i! Wacici!' Wacici heard him and she felt so happy that he had come to liberate her. She answered quickly, 'Yuu-uuu!' At once her brother started digging and removing the soil. He dug and dug until he came to where she was sitting and crying. He carried her to the surface and examined her: she was in good shape except that she had weakened because of hunger and fear. He took her home and her parents were so happy to see her again. She was given a good bath and a lamb was slaughtered to offer thanksgiving to Mwene-Nyaga who had preserved her life.

Wacici reported what her friends had done to her. The following morning the evil girls were arrested and sent to a trial before the elders in a tribunal court and their fathers were heavily fined. They had to pay many heads of cattle and many rams and bulls were slaughtered and a lot of beer had to be brewed for the judges and the elders to eat and drink. The bad girls were exposed and they were all shunned in society and were unable to get husbands for a long time. Wacici was widely respected and she got married and became a mother of many children and lived happily ever after.

The Wise Man and his Sons

A LONG time ago there was a wise old man who was respected throughout Kenya because of his great wisdom. He was one of the greatest judges of his time. He presided over many tribal courts and councils. He was rich and noble, but he lived a simple life, and was very kind and helpful to his fellow countrymen. Not a man sought his help in vain. Children of his neighbourhood frequented his house to hear his wonderful stories and advice. They regarded him as their father. He was loved by the children as well as by the grown-ups.

When he grew old and feeble and realized that his days were coming to an end, he called his six sons to his bedside to deliver his will.

'My dear sons,' he said, 'I am growing old and weak, and one of these days I am going to die and leave you to take care of my wealth and perpetuate this family. I have great confidence in you, but I want to warn you that unless you live in unity and harmony you could easily get destroyed by your enemies.'

'We promise you, father,' they replied, 'that we shall live in unity, and that we shall uphold the respect you gained over the years, and we shall take care of this family and defend our property.'

'Yes, my sons,' he said, 'I know that you will, but I want to tell you the old story of the three foolish cows, who were deceived and destroyed by the clever lion.

'Once upon a time,' he began, 'cows lived in the wilderness like other wild beasts. They grazed in the jungle in large herds,

94

and were not afraid of the other animals. But they were constantly attacked by the other strong beasts like lions, leopards, elephants, and when the cows realized that they could not live in peace in the jungle they decided to seek help from men. They all agreed to live under the protection of men except for three stupid sister cows. Their names were Ndune (Red), Nyange (White), and Nguno (Hornless). Ndune was as red as ochre and her eyes were fierce and had sparks like fire when she was angry. Her horns were long, sharp, and strong, and she could scare any beast. Ndune was loved by her sisters dearly. Nyange had a white coat, as white as snow. She also had fierce horns, but looked more peaceful than Ndune, and was not so much feared, but when she was angry her white fur became whiter, and blinding to other animals. Nguno looked like a clown without horns, and annoyed other animals who regarded her as an abnormal creature of God who should not be attacked.

'I think you know this story,' he said.

'Yes,' they replied, 'but please continue, father.'

'One day Lion, who was very clever, decided to divide the three sister cows, kill them one by one, and eat them. Lion had tried to catch them before, but the three cows had fought and killed many beasts. Nyange and Nguno would charge their assailant from back and front while Ndune would come from the side and, with her sharp fierce horns, pierce the enemy's stomach, tear it open, and kill him instantly. Lion could not kill any of them unless he divided them and attacked them separately.

'So one day the clever lion went and spoke to Ndune. He told her that she was respected in the jungle for her fierce horns and her beautiful red coat. He told her that if she lived apart from her sisters she would never be attacked by anyone. She would be made the duchess of the whole jungle kingdom. Her sisters were very ugly and annoying, and that is why the three of them were constantly attacked. Ndune was very much tempted to leave her sisters when she heard what the clever lion told her. Next the lion went to Nyange and praised her beauty.

He told her that she was born a peacemaker because of her white coat, and that she should have spent much of her time seeking peace in the jungle. He told her that if she left her fierce and domineering sister Ndune, and also avoid the company of her monstrous and abnormal sister Nguno, then Lion would make her the beauty queen of the jungle and find her a good husband there. Nyange was flattered and started to think about the idea of living apart from her sisters.

'Finally Lion went to see Nguno. He told her that she was the most peaceful cow that ever existed, and that she was highly respected for her elegant hornless head. It was risky on her part to live with her sisters who were constantly attacked by savage beasts because of their fierce horns and provocative coats. Lion promised to protect Nguno if she deserted her sisters at once. Nguno, who was getting tired of fighting ceaseless battles was happy at this friendly gesture, and at once decided to desert her sisters without pausing to think it over.

'No sooner did she leave her sisters than she was caught by Lion and killed.

'Nyange also slipped away from Ndune the following day and went to look for Lion so that she could be made the jungle queen of beauty. She too was caught and killed. Now Ndune was left alone, and she also was caught and killed. That was the fate of the three stupid cows. Had they continued to live to-gether in unity, they would have lived.'

'It is a very good story, father,' said the six sons, 'and it has a great lesson in it. We shall continue to live in unity.'

'Good, my sons,' the old man continued, 'I am very pleased to hear that, and I know that you will not let me down. I have one more example to show you; come closer.' At this point he showed them six sticks, equal in size. He gave one to each of the sons. 'Break them in two, please,' he commanded. The sons broke the sticks at one go. He asked them to break them into smaller bits, and this they did. Then he produced a bundle of six sticks of similar size and thickness. These were properly bound together with one strong string. He gave the bundle to his sons, and asked them to pass it to one another, to examine it closely and see how it was bound. Then he asked them to break the bundle, and they all tried one after the other. None of them could manage to break the bundle, and he took it back intact.

'You see, my sons, each one of you is like those cows or these sticks,' he said. 'If you are not united you will be destroyed like the three cows who were devoured by Lion, or like the six sticks you have just destroyed. But if you stay together like this bundle of sticks, you will defeat your enemies, and you will be able to protect your property and sustain this family.'

'Yes, father,' replied his sons, 'unity is strength, and we shall always remain united.'

He died a happy man and proud of his sons, who from that time lived in unity and harmony, and like their father were loved and respected by many people.

Wacu and the Eagle

A LONG time ago there was a girl who ate meat in public like a boy. Her name was Wacu and she was the only child in her family. Her father was a rich man with many heads of cattle, many goats, and flocks of sheep. Wacu grazed the sheep and cattle and goats in the fields and milked them in the evening just like boys did. Her father loved her very much and he gave her meat to eat and milk to drink. She developed the habits of a boy. This used to annoy her mother who wanted to bring her up as a good woman and housewife.

The influence of her father dominated Wacu so much that she became ever more boyish and her mother could not easily change her. In the evenings she stayed with her father in *thingira* (father's hut), eating meat and listening to his advice and stories. During the day Wacu grazed the animals and played games like wrestling and long jump with the boys. She was feared by many boys as she defeated many of them. She was widely known throughout the villages as the strong boyish girl who fought and defeated boys.

When Wacu grew up and was initiated into the grown-up age group, as was the custom, she had to give up herding and do domestic work. It was very difficult to rehabilitate her. She could not stop eating meat and drinking milk publicly like a man. For this habit she was shunned by other girls. Friends in her age group got married and Wacu needed to have a husband. A woman of Wacu's habits would find it very difficult to find a lover because Gikuyu custom did not allow women to eat meat publicly.

99

Wacu's mother complained to her husband that he was spoiling her daughter. He began to realize his mistake too late, for Wacu was widely known as a he-woman. She was strong and hard-working, and above all she was very pretty. Meat eating, hardwork, and games had helped to build her body well. But even with these natural physical gifts the boys would not propose to Wacu; they regarded her as a meat maniac.

Wacu gave up the idea of getting married, and went back to her favourite work of herding her father's animals. She continued to eat meat without any secrecy and she even slaughtered sheep whenever she wanted to have meat. She wanted to make the best out of her situation.

One day Wacu visited a relative who lived in a distant part of the Gikuyu country and while she was there she went to dances in the evenings with other young people. There she met a handsome young man who admired her and proposed to her almost immediately. Wacu accepted him. She returned home and reported the young man's proposal to her parents. They approved. Arrangements were made for the payment of the marriage dowries and the wedding ceremonies and Wacu was quickly wedded before her husband had time to discover her propensity to eat meat.

For some time after her marriage Wacu tried her level best to uphold the manners and customs of a young bride. She would not eat meat, nor would she drink milk or eat fried food. This was too much of a sacrifice for Wacu who was brought up eating all these delicacies. When she could not control herself she bought meat secretly in the market-place, cooked it quietly in her hut and ate it while her husband was at beer parties.

Wacu was a good housewife, hard-working and strong. She bore her husband many children—all boys. When she was sure that she could not get divorced because she had good children she decided to revert to her habit of eating meat publicly without any fear. She did not see why women should be so badly treated by their menfolk. So she declared an open campaign against this injustice of men to women. She became most unpopular with men, and her husband was greatly disturbed because he loved her and her children. He pleaded with her to observe the custom, but it was all useless for Wacu would not be stopped from eating meat.

Wacu's husband went and consulted many witch-doctors to find out what he could do to cure her of this bad habit. They advised him not ever to give her any meat, even if he slaughtered for the customary family religious ceremonies—the occasions at which wives were given meat by their menfolk.

Wacu defied this ban. She would buy her own meat from the market and bring it home. When she did not have money to buy any and her husband slaughtered and denied her the right to eat the meat, she cried and cursed him:

Uu-uúuuu!	'Uu-uuuuu!
Ninguga mbu;	I shall curse;
Mucii uyu wene,	This strange homestead;
Nanguritwo;	Though I'm betrothed and
Naigathinjwo;	married;
Nandiheo.	They have slaughtered;
Uu-uuuuu!'	And I have not been fed.
	Uu-uuuuu!'

Wacu knew that this cry was regarded as a bad omen for women to make, and in order to cleanse the homestead a lamb had to be slaughtered and she would be given the meat to quieten the bad spirits. Each time she cried like this the husband slaughtered a lamb and she was given the meat. She really became a nuisance to the whole family, yet she was blessed with so many children that the husband could not bear to see her returned to her father. So she was tolerated.

One day the Gikuyu elders were having a feast of goats and lambs. This feast was held in the field far away from the homesteads. The young men slaughtered and roasted meat while the elders discussed and debated the affairs of the people. Some elders had come with the motions and proposals that women should be given more rights and especially the right to share meat with their menfolk, so that a situation like Wacu's could be avoided in future. Wacu was greatly admired for her hard work, sense of duty, fertility, and beauty, except the one unfortunate characteristic—the love of eating meat. Examples of Masai women were cited to support the motion, and there was a heated debate. The echo of the noise these elders made could be heard over the hill tops.

While this debate was going on the young men were roasting the meat, and when it was well done they put it on green banana leaves to cool a little before the elders could share it. Suddenly an enormous eagle appeared in the sky. It came with such force that it frightened the elders and the young men. It was most strange and quite different from anything men had seen before. The elders and the young men took cover to avoid being carried off by this great eagle.

The eagle came down and with its big claws and beak carried all the roasted carcasses, leaving nothing for the men. Then it disappeared over the hill into the horizon. Some young men ran after it to see if it would drop any meat. They followed it fast over the hill, down the valley, and through a field, and they could see the eagle far away, landing or going low as though it were landing.

They ran faster. The eagle in fact had come to the field where Wacu was weeding. Just a few feet away from her the eagle dropped all the meat and flew away, disappearing into the forest of Kiri-Nyaga. When the young men reached Wacu they found her comfortably sitting down, feasting on the meat. They were surprised and horrified and would not take the meat from her. They returned quickly to the elders to report what they had seen.

The elders came to verify the young men's report, and when they saw that it was Wacu, and that the eagle had dropped all the meat down to her, they all resolved to give their women the right to eat meat in their homesteads, as it was the wish of Mwene-Nyaga that they should have meat. *Ciakorire Wacu mugunda* (Meat found Wacu in the field) is a common joke when one meets some luck without much effort.

The Story of Ragai and his Wife

ONCE upon a time there was a peasant who was so well-known for his trickery and fraudulence that people nick-named him 'Ragai', which means 'Liar'. He was notorious throughout Kenya and East Africa.

Ragai lived in poor, semi-desert country where there was very little rain, but he had a small stretch of ground which was about the best in the whole district, because he could irrigate it from the near-by river and grow some crops on it. During the long drought there was little water for irrigation.

Ragai had a very attractive wife, but for a long time they had no children. They consulted all the good and famous witch-doctors from far and near to find out the reason for this and what they should do in order to have a child. They went to a lot of expense to pay the doctors' fees and to buy all the things prescribed for the sacrifices advised by the witch-doctors. Thank God, at last Ragai's wife bore him a son.

Whether this was because of the magic power of the witch-doctor or by the will of God, or merely by luck, Ragai and his wife believed and respected the witch-doctors more deeply than ever.

Ragai's wife loved her son more than anything else in the world. Like any father, Ragai too loved his son greatly. When he was not on his shamba, his small farm cultivated for family subsistence, irrigating or weeding, he spent most of his time swindling people. Therefore he saw very little of his family during the day.

One day Ragai managed to buy a small calf from a traveller.

He built it a nice stable near the house and fed it on hay, corn, and anything else he could get which was good for cattle. Nobody else in his district had a cow, so there was plenty of food for the young animal. He bought chaff from his neighbours and the animal grew very fast and well and in no time Ragai had a fat cow.

As there were no other cattle in his district, he could not breed from his animal. Instead he intended to fatten it and slaughter it, sell the meat and start a business with the money he would make from it. Ragai was very confident about his plan.

One day he travelled to a distant market-place to look for a slaughter-house. He had to be away for a week.

On the same day that Ragai left for the market-place, his son, who was about two years old now, was taken ill with an attack of mumps and influenza. On the following day the child seemed very ill and Ragai's wife, quite ignorant of children's diseases, thought that her son was in danger of his life. But she could not get hold of her husband to go and see a doctor and find out the cause of the illness and the best way to cure it.

Now her neighbours were jealous both of Ragai's beautiful wife and his cow. But without thinking about the neighbour's past bitter experience of her husband's dishonesty, she called one who she thought was on friendly terms with her and her husband and gave him some money to go and consult a witch-doctor.

Taking the money and promising to do his best to help, the man went out. He gathered a few of his friends together and they conspired to deceive Mrs Ragai, for the man knew that the child was only suffering from mumps and would be well in a couple of days.

They decided to ask one of the bad witch-doctors to co-operate with them in deceiving Mrs Ragai, in revenge for what Ragai had done to them in the past. They got hold of a doctor and planned to tell Mrs Ragai that the cause of the child's illness was the cow at the house. They would say that the cow was spiritually unclean, that it should be slaughtered at once, its meat given freely to the neighbours and the child, and the house sprinkled with its blood, and that then the child would get better at once.

With this plan the man returned and told this story to Ragai's wife. Believing him there and then, she asked the man to bring the witch-doctor along the following day, together with all the neighbours.

Very early the next morning his men were there, but only those involved in the conspiracy were invited by him. The doctor came a little late, saying how busy he was, and he ordered his followers to bring out the cow. He produced his magic paraphernalia and walked round the cow seven times and facing the sun he asked his god to cure the child as soon as the cow had been killed. This ceremonial spectacle was an ordeal for Mrs Ragai, but she was most anxious to see her son well again.

When the cow was slaughtered, the child was sprinkled with the blood as the doctor had prescribed, and the meat was given freely to all the neighbours present. Of course the doctor and his attendants helped themselves to the best parts of the carcass and hardly any meat was left for Ragai's family.

Next morning the young Ragai was crying for food. Mrs Ragai fed him delightedly. By the end of the day he was running about and playing as usual. What magic! She had no doubt this was because of the wonderful treatment given by the witch-doctor. She missed the cow, but she did not regret having complied with the doctor's prescription.

The next day Ragai returned, having made plans for the slaughter of the cow and reserved a slaughter-house at the market-place. Approaching his house by the gate of the homestead, he saw a lot of blood and banana leaves which had been used for the ceremony. He was very puzzled. He stood still gazing at the scene, and suddenly his wife saw him standing there. She hurried to welcome him home and told him the wonderful news of their son's recovery; but when he heard how his cow had been slaughtered he was terribly angry. For he knew that most of the men she mentioned, including the witch-doctor himself, were his enemies.

He wanted to send his wife back to her parents and live without her. He told her that she was the most stupid woman in the world.

'How do you know?' asked his wife. Unable to answer her question, Ragai decided to leave his family for some time and travel the world over to study women and to see if they were all such fools as his wife. He told her that if he found them intelligent he would divorce her and marry another one, but that if they were fools like her, he would keep her.

She beseeched him to forgive her and forget, but he would not listen to any apologies, and went away. Travelling through many countries, Ragai met women of all nationalities. He deceived many and made a lot of money. But he did not want to return home until he had reached a very famous country he had heard of. It was a long way, but Ragai was determined to see that country and its women; particularly the king's wife, who was said to be very beautiful.

When he got to this country he made a special study of the royal family. People were pleased to see a foreigner so fond of the royal family and keenly interested in the history of the country. They were especially helpful to Ragai as they thought that his knowledge and experience might be of use in improving relations between their two countries. Ragai was very pleased with his successes.

He now heard of an old woman who lived not very far from the royal palace. She was said to be a centenarian. She once worked in the royal household and she knew the family history inside out.

Ragai went to this woman disguised as a priest and told her that he would pay her a big sum of money if she took him into her house and taught him the history of the royal family. The woman was only too pleased to teach Ragai and to help him in any way she could. She refused to accept his money but asked him to be good and helpful to other people as a priest.

Ragai mastered his knowledge of the royal history and knew

it so well that people hardly believed that he was a foreigner and not one of the members of the royal household itself. He knew the names of all the ancestors of the royal family, their servants, what they used to do when alive, and so forth. He knew the names of all its living members, all the particulars about each and every one of them; their servants, their maids, their estates, etc.

After mastering these details, Ragai now studied the movements of the ruling king, who used to tour his country along with his soldiers in certain seasons of the year. Usually he left the queen behind to look after the affairs of the palace. Ragai knew that one day the king was going away on his customary tour. In the morning Ragai left the old woman's house very early without telling her where he was going. He dressed himself in rags, entered the palace gates, and hid in the garden. He saw the rubbish pit which was immediately below the kitchen window. He went there and buried himself under the rubbish. Sometimes the queen liked to make her own food when the king was not in the palace.

The queen opened the window that morning while making breakfast. She threw some kitchen waste through the window into the pit, and, gazing at the flowers in the garden and admiring the beauty of the morning sunshine, to her surprise and horror suddenly saw a dusty, ragged man stretch himself and stand up in the pit! It was a terrible sight! She could not believe her eyes. She thought she was in a dream, but a voice said to her,

'Please be calm, your majesty. I come here with good news from your ancestors.' Mentioning the names of all the dead members of the royal family and their servants and maids, he delivered their greetings and good wishes to the royal household and all those members of the royal family who were living. The queen bowed down and asked the good messenger to enter the palace. She made him a nice breakfast and, sitting in the royal lodge, Ragai told the queen that he was the old chief steward of the late king who had died a hundred years before. He had been sent by the royal family from the next world back to this world, to tell them here how this most famous royal family was now living in disgrace because of poverty. They needed some money, gold, silver, diamonds, kingly golden robes, crowns, and royal clothes sent to them. Royal people of other nations were well looked after there by their descendants on this earth. They demanded that they should be well provided for or they would cast bad spirits into the whole kingdom.

The queen, terrified at this news, at once ordered a servant to pack all that the messenger wanted from the house. As the things Ragai wanted to take were beyond his strength to carry, he asked the queen to give him one of the best horses in the royal stable. She gave him anything that he wanted, including gold, and jewellery, and other precious things. He loaded his horse and rode off.

Next day the king returned to the palace. The queen, welcoming him home, told him of the ghostly messenger from their dead relations from the next world. She told him of the things she had given him including some of his best golden crowns and robes.

The king was furious. He told his queen that the messenger was a clever thief, and started off at once on his horse to pursue him. He asked the queen to send more people to follow him, but he did not want to waste any time waiting for them. He was experienced in battle, and confident that he could fight the thief on his own if only he could find him.

He followed the trail and the dung of the horse and travelled day and night. His soldiers were now following him, but they were many miles behind him.

One morning, tracking through a semi-desert country-side, he saw a horse in the distance. He was sure it was the thief with his horse, as he had not lost the trail. He rode even faster and faster.

Now riding through the desert by night, Ragai's horse sustained a serious sprain from falling into an ant-hole. This was a tragedy for Ragai. He looked back and saw the king pursuing him. He was certainly a good liar, but he had not been to the army school where sword fighting was perfected. He had a sword, a golden sword from the royal house, but it was no good to him if he had to fight the king.

While worrying what to do, whether to abandon the horse and run away with a little money or whether just to run for his life, he saw by the side of the track a peasant dressed in rags working in his shamba and near him a very tall tree.

Without losing any time, Ragai went to this man and, offering to pay him a good sum of money, asked him to exchange his clothes for his own, and to take the horse and tether it under the tree and then to climb the tree, and stay for a few minutes at the top, while Ragai worked in the shamba like a peasant. He said it was great fun for him as he was bored with being a king, and would pay any amount of money just for this amusement.

The peasant, thrilled with the idea of getting so much money for doing such an easy job, complied with the 'king's' wishes at once. Ragai started to work in the shamba. He soiled his body as much and as quickly as he could. He still saw the cloud of dust of the king's horse come nearer and nearer; but the poor peasant on the tree did not understand what all this was about.

In a few minutes the king was there, and as he did not see the horse lying tired under the tree with a pain in its injured foot, asked Ragai if he had seen a man passing by on horseback. Ragai stood up and instead of answering the king he pretended to be shocked and surprised to see a king speaking to him. Feigning shyness, he looked around silently, and the king looking around until he saw what Ragai was looking at, discovered the horse under the tree, and almost at the same instant the horse smelled the king's horse and whinnied. The king gladly went to it and examined it; he could see at once that it was his own horse he was pursuing. Then he spoke to Ragai again,

'Have you seen the man who had this horse?' Again the 'peasant' was shy; he shook his head, looked up and pointed to the neatly dressed man at the top of the tree.

'No doubt this is the thief.'

'Come down, you thief and I shall cut you into pieces! shouted the king. The man did not answer. The king asked

Ragai to climb the tree and bring the thief down. Apologetically Ragai told the king that his religion did not permit him to climb trees, but if the king wished to climb the tree himself Ragai would hold his robes and the horse for him. The king at once took off his shoes and robes and started to climb the tree. It was a very tall tree. When the king was about half way or three-quarters up, Ragai took his load from the limping horse on to the king's horse and with the king's robes and shoes rode off at a terrific speed.

When the king saw this, he did not know whether to climb higher and get the man on the tree or to go down and chase the other man who had his property. He decided to do the latter. He quickly came down and tried to ride the other horse, but of course he found the horse could not move. He examined the hooves and found that the horse had a sprain. In the meantime the man on the tree came down quickly to explain to the king what had happened, and realizing that he had been deceived, the king gave up and began to walk slowly homeward with his lame horse.

The following day he met some of his men who had come to help him, but ashamed of his folly, the king was determined not to pursue the chase any longer, but to return home.

Back at his palace he told his queen that the ghostly man was a genuine messenger from the dead, and that he also had given him more clothes and a better horse, as his was injured. The queen was very pleased to hear this and now believed that her family would live happily ever after.

Ragai got home with his newly-acquired wealth, and when his wife asked him where and how he had obtained such a treasure, he told her that he was more than convinced now that all women the world over were like herself.

'They are all pleasant fools,' he said. They bought more land, built luxurious houses, and lived happily ever after.

Wahome and the First White Hunter

WAHOME was a Gikuyu hunter whose home was at Chinga in Nyeri. Like most other professional hunters his livelihood depended entirely on hunting. He was a very big man in stature and he was always compared with or spoken of as a giant. He could fight lions, leopards, and antelopes with his bare hands. He was feared greatly by many people throughout Nyeri, and the fame of his courage and strength spread all over the Gikuyu country.

When the first European hunter came to Gikuyuland, he sought the help of Gikuyu hunters to guide him in the Nyandarwa mountains* where he wanted to go to shoot lions, leopards, and elephants. The white hunter was informed that Wahome would be the most suitable and helpful companion for him.

The white hunter trekked through the Gikuyu country and reached Nyeri where he met Wahome. He was introduced to him by other Agikuyu porters he had brought with him. Wahome could not believe that the white man was really a hunter as he looked so small in comparison to Wahome himself. Wahome rejected the idea of joining the white man as a hunting companion as he thought that the white hunter could surely not manage to handle a lion or leopard as Wahome would. But the white man explained to Wahome that he had a rifle and a shotgun and that he would have very little to do with

* Aberdare Hills.

his bare hands. (The whole conversation was done through an interpreter who spoke to Bwana the white hunter in Swahili.)

Convinced that the white man was a real hunter, Wahome agreed to join Bwana in his hunting safaris. This was the first time Wahome had ever seen a white man, let alone a white hunter. He was very happy to have the opportunity to see the white man's weapons, which were spoken of as magic sticks which spat fire and killed animals at great distances. Wahome wanted to examine them closely, learn how to use them, and possibly possess them one day.

The contract was signed and Bwana and Wahome seemed to like each other immensely. Each was a great asset to the other. Bwana had magic weapons which Wahome admired much; Wahome on the other hand was a giant, he knew the forests around Nyandarwa and Kiri-Nyaga* very well and he understood the habits of different animals, which Bwana did not. So they both needed each other very badly. But there was one great barrier between them. They did not speak a common language. Bwana spoke English and Swahili whereas Wahome spoke his mother tongue (Gikuyu) only. Wahome had learnt a little broken Swahili and he managed to master phrases such as *ndiyo, Bwana; jambo Bwana* or 'yes, sir; how do you do, sir;' but he could not express himself in Swahili or understand much of what Bwana would tell him. Yet Wahome was a very proud man and did not like to show Bwana that he did not understand him. This language barrier was not taken seriously by Bwana as he wanted Wahome for his hunting ability and skill and not for language or any other refined academic knowledge.

One day they both went to hunt lions in Nyandarwa forests. Bwana had a very big Alsatian who also was a great hunter. The dog was trained to attack animals as soon as Bwana shot them. It jumped and fought wounded animals the moment Bwana had fired a shot.

Bwana, Wahome, and the dog trekked through the forest until they came to a place where they saw a big lion basking in the sun. Bwana asked Wahome to hold the dog tight while he

* Mount Kenya.

fired and to release the dog as soon as Bwana had fired and said *wacha mbwa* (let the dog loose) loudly. Bwana had to shoot again and again until the lion was killed. The dog had to charge the wounded lion to stop it coming close to Bwana.

Bwana fired and called and told Wahome to let the dog loose; *Wahome wacha mbwa! Wacha mbwa Wahome!* Bwana repeated his call to Wahome, and at this time the dog was barking furiously and trying to free itself from Wahome's hands. Wahome held it tighter and tighter as it struggled. Bwana hopelessly repeated his call, *Wahome wacha mbwa*, but without success. He managed to shoot the lion dead when it almost got to him. It was hardly fifty yards when Bwana shot it in the head. It was a great relief to Bwana to see the lion fall dead, but he was very angry with his hunting companion Wahome.

Each time he had called out *Wahome wacha mbwa*, Wahome replied in Gikuyu *Bwana, nongamatite no kigathi ireketie*, that is, 'Sir, I am still holding tight, but the dog is very naughty and troublesome.' Wahome said it several times in reply to Bwana's call to release the dog and each time he said it in a tone similar to what Swahili should sound like and hoped that Bwana would understand. But neither Bwana nor Wahome understood what the other had said.

Bwana came and asked Wahome why he did not release the dog; Wahome repeated his answer that he was still holding the dog tight, but that the dog was disobedient. He slapped Wahome in the face and Wahome kept on saying the dog was at fault. Bwana hit Wahome again and again and very furiously. Wahome did not retaliate in any way and kept quiet. *Wewe mjinga!* or 'you are a fool', Bwana said to Wahome as he slapped him. To Wahome *wewe mjinga* sounded like the Gikuyu phrase *wee wi mu-Chinga* or 'you are from Chinga'.

I Bwana to ta Ngai; nioi gwitu no Chinga! or 'Bwana is like God; he knows I am from Chinga!' Wahome replied.

A man who witnessed the whole episode from a distance called out loudly and said,

'Fight back, Wahome, fight back!'

'No! I shan't. If I hit the white man I shall wound his delicate white skin and I shall be imprisoned for it.'

'Then run away, Wahome. Run away. The white man will cripple you. Run away, Wahome!' the man repeated his advice to Wahome, and all this time Bwana was slapping Wahome like mad.

'Oh no!' Wahome replied 'the white man would think I am a coward, I shall not run away. I shall not show him my back! I am not a woman!'

When Bwana realized that Wahome did not know Swahili at all and that he had not appreciated anything he had told him he decided to do without Wahome's services. Wahome had to return to Chinga, where he had come from to join Bwana in his hunting expeditions.

That was the end of Wahome's hunting pact with the first white hunter in the Gikuyu country. Their story has been told repeatedly throughout Gikuyu country and has delighted and caused laughter to many up to the present day.

Published by Transafrica Publishers Limited, Kenwood House, Kimathi Street, P.O. Box 42990, Nairobi, Kenya and printed by Printing and Packaging Corporation Limited, P.O. Box 30157, Likoni Road, Nairobi, Kenya